Essential Ch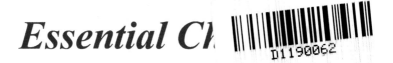

ELECTRONIC STRUCTURE
AND
THE PERIODIC TABLE

A Self-Teaching Guide

3rd edition

STERLING
Education

STERLING
Education

3   2   1

ISBN-13: 978-1-9475569-1-1

Sterling Education
6 Liberty Square #11
Boston, MA 02109

info@sterling–prep.com

From the foundations of chemical reactions to complex mechanisms of atomic particles, the *Essential Chemistry Self-Teaching Guide* series is a perfect compendium to provide readers with the information required to understand multifaceted chemistry topics.

This series is a detailed review of the fundamental processes and mechanisms affecting general chemistry and physical processes at the atomic level. The content was designed to elucidate the concepts of the electronic structure of elements, principles of chemical bonding, phases of matter, types and mechanisms of chemical reactions, stoichiometry, acid-base equilibria, solution chemistry, thermochemistry, and electrochemistry.

Created by highly qualified science teachers, researchers, and education specialists, this book empowers both the average and the well-informed readers to develop and expand their understanding of general chemistry.

We commend your desire to learn more about the principles of general chemistry. The editors sincerely hope that these guides will be a valuable resource for your learning.

Your purchase helps support global environmental causes

Sterling Test Prep is committed to protecting our planet by supporting environmental organizations committed to conservation, research, and preservation of vital natural resources. Your purchase helps support these organizations so they can continue their critical missions.

The Ocean Conservancy advocates for a healthy ocean with sustainable solutions based on science and cleanup efforts.

The Rainforest Trust saves critical lands for conservation through land purchases and protected area designations in over 16 countries.

Pacific Whale Foundation saves whales from extinction and protects our oceans through science and advocacy.

Highest quality guarantee

Be the first to report a content error for a $10 reward
or a grammatical mistake to receive a $5 reward.

info@sterling–prep.com

*We reply to all emails – **check your spam folder***

Electronic Structure and the Periodic Table

Table of Contents

Electronic Structure and the Periodic Table

Table of Contents (*continued*)

Essential Chemistry Self-Teaching Guide series

- Electronic Structure and the Periodic Table

- Chemical Bonding

- Phases and Phase Equilibria

- Stoichiometry

- Kinetics and Equilibrium in Chemical Reactions

- Acids and Bases

- Solution Chemistry

- Thermochemistry and Thermodynamics

- Electrochemistry

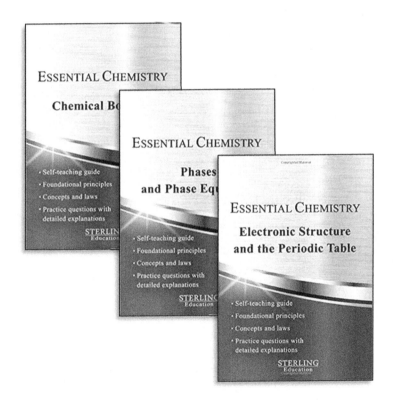

Essential Physics Self-Teaching Guide series

- Kinematics and Dynamics

- Equilibrium and Momentum

- Force, Motion, Gravitation

- Work and Energy

- Fluids and Solids

- Waves and Periodic Motion

- Light and Optics

- Sound

- Electrostatics and Electromagnetism

- Electric Circuits

- Heat and Thermodynamics

- Atomic and Nuclear Structure

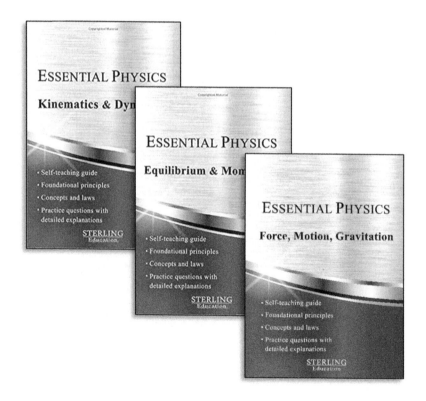

Essential Biology Self-Teaching Guide series

- Eukaryotic Cell: Structure and Function
- Enzymes and Cellular Metabolism
- DNA, Protein Synthesis, Gene Expression
- Specialized Eukaryotic Cells
- Genetics
- Nervous System
- Endocrine System
- Circulatory System
- Respiratory System
- Lymphatic and Immune System
- Digestive System
- Excretory System
- Skeletal System
- Muscle System
- Integumentary System
- Reproductive System
- Development
- Microbiology
- Plants
- Photosynthesis
- Evolution, Classification, Diversity
- Ecosystems and Biosphere
- Population and Community Ecology

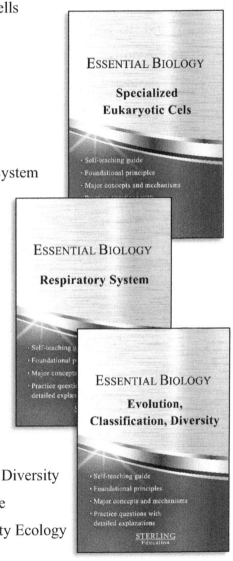

Everything You Always Wanted to Know About...

- American History
- American Law
- American Government and Politics
- Comparative Government and Politics
- World History
- European History
- Psychology
- Environmental Science
- Human Geography

Electronic Structure and the Periodic Table

Topic Review

Electronic Structure

The *atom* is the smallest unit of an element that retains the characteristics of that element. An atom consists of several *subatomic particles*, including protons, neutrons, and electrons.

The *nucleus* is the densely packed region at the center of an atom that consists of protons and neutrons. The diameter of the nucleus is approximately ~10,000 times smaller than the overall diameter of the atom. Most of an atom's volume comes from its *electron cloud*, the outer region surrounding the nucleus.

The *proton* is the positively charged particle located in the nucleus of the atom. Each proton has a charge of +1, and its mass is approximately equal to a neutron.

The *neutron* is an uncharged particle in the nucleus of the atom.

The *electron* is a small, negatively charged particle located in the electron cloud. Each electron has a charge of –1, and its mass is about 2,000 times smaller than a proton or neutron. In a neutral atom, the number of electrons equals the number of protons.

The *electrostatic attraction* (i.e., due to opposite electrostatic charges) between the positive core protons and orbiting negative electrons holds electrons around the nucleus. The *repulsion* between neighboring electrons spreads them over the entire volume of the electron cloud.

An *ion* forms when an atom loses or gains electrons, causing the atom to have either a net negative or a net positive charge. The loss of electrons produces positively charged *cations*, and the gain of electrons produces negatively charged *anions*.

Cations and anions are represented by a superscript of a positive or negative sign after a chemical symbol.

The *atomic number* (*Z*) equals the number of protons in an atom. If the atom has no charge, then *Z* equals the number of electrons. On the periodic table, elements are arranged by their atomic numbers.

The *mass number* (A) is the total number of protons and neutrons (i.e., *nucleons*) of an atom.

Isotopes are atoms of the same element with the same number of protons (i.e., same atomic number Z) but a different number of neutrons. Therefore, isotopes have different mass numbers A. The isotope of an atom has virtually identical chemical properties as the atom because they have the same number of protons and therefore are the same element.

Most elements naturally occur as a mixture of two or more stable isotopes. For example, the element carbon ($Z=6$) includes the isotopes ^{12}carbon, ^{13}carbon, and ^{14}carbon. The 12, 13, and 14 are the mass numbers (A) of the respective isotopes. ^{12}Carbon has six neutrons, ^{13}carbon has seven neutrons, and ^{14}carbon has eight neutrons.

The *relative atomic mass* of an element (also known as *atomic weight*) is the weighted average of the masses of its stable isotopes.

Mass spectrometry is an experimental method used to determine the atomic masses of isotopes. In mass spectrometry, a sample is ionized by bombarding it with electrons, which causes it to break into charged fragments. Ions separate when subjected to an electric or magnetic field. The amount of deflection the ions experience is proportional to the ions' mass.

The unit of measurement used for atomic weight is the *atomic mass unit* (amu) or *dalton* (Da), which is approximately equivalent to the mass of one nucleon (a single proton and neutron). The dalton is based on the atomic mass of the carbon-12 isotope, meaning 1 amu is equal to 1/12 the mass of a ^{12}C atom or 1.66×10^{-27} g.

^{12}Carbon is the only atomic species with an atomic mass that is strictly a whole number. The atomic masses of other elements are always remarkably close to the atomic mass units' whole numbers.

Atomic mass is expressed by the equation:

avg. atomic mass $= (mass_1) \cdot (abundance_1) + (mass_2) \cdot (abundance_2) + \ldots$

Hydrogen has two isotopes; masses and abundances are shown below:

Isotope	Mass	% Abundance
^{1}H	1.0078 amu	99.985
^{2}H	2.0140 amu	0.015000

The relative atomic mass of hydrogen (i.e., atomic weight) is:

$$(0.99985 \times 1.0078 \text{ amu}) + (0.00015000 \times 2.0140 \text{ amu})$$

$$1.0076 + 0.00030210 = 1.0079 \text{ amu for H}$$

Orbital structure of hydrogen atom, principal quantum number *n*, number of electrons per orbital

The *electron configuration* of an atom is the arrangement of electrons around the nucleus. Electron configurations describe electrons as each moving independently in a predefined orbital around the nucleus.

Nobel laureate Niels Bohr (1885-1962), a Danish physicist of the 20th century, was the first to apply quantum physics, using wave functions, to define the electrons' energy discrete values. A single-electron atom is an elementary particle that consists of one electron around its core nucleus of a proton and a neutron. The *Bohr model*, discussed in more detail later, focuses on the hydrogen atom and the single electron that orbits its nucleus. In quantum mechanics, the hydrogen electron exists in a spherical probability density cloud around its nucleus.

The *principal quantum number* (*n*) defines which shell the electron occupies and describes the orbital's *size* and distance from the nucleus. The principal quantum number has only positive integer values of $n = 1, 2, 3...$

Electron shells, called principal energy levels, are labeled by their principal quantum numbers ($n = 1, 2, 3...$), but can be labeled alphabetically as $n = $ K, L, M...

Higher *n* shells indicate larger orbitals further from the nucleus and higher energy levels. The maximum number of electrons per shell is $2n^2$.

For example, the second shell can hold up to $2(2)^2 = 8$ electrons.

Electrons usually occupy outer shells only after inner shells have filled. However, some outer shell electrons are promoted to a higher shell if it imparts stability to the atom.

Conventional notation for electronic structure

The *Aufbau principle* states that electrons fill their orbitals in the order of lowest energy to highest energy. Orbitals fill according to the diagonal lines shown.

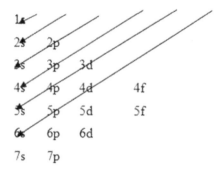

$$1s^2\ 2s^2\ 2p^6\ 3s^2\ 3p^6\ 4s^2\ 3d^{10}\ 4p^6\ 5s^2\ 4d^{10}\ 5p^6\ 6s^2\ 4f^{14}\ 5d^{10}\ 6p^6\ 7s^2\ 5f^{14}\ 6d^{10}\ 7p^6$$

In multi-electron atoms, the energy level for an electron is affected by both the *n* and *l* quantum numbers. The *l* quantum number is discussed later but know that it is represented by the letters *s, p, d,* and *f.* The *l* quantum number describes a subshell. Subshells are comprised of atomic orbitals, and each orbital can hold two electrons.

The 4*s* orbital is lower in energy than the 3*d* orbitals. From the *Aufbau principle,* electrons populate the 4*s* orbital before the 3*d* orbital, even though the 4*s* orbital has a higher principal (*n*) value than the 3*d* orbital.

Hund's rule is another essential guideline for writing electron configurations. Hund's rule states that an electron must occupy every orbital in a sublevel (e.g., s, p, d, f) before a second electron can occupy an orbital in that sublevel. Hund's rule maximizes the number of electrons with the same electron magnetic spin (discussed below) to increase the atom's stability. Double-occupied orbitals are much higher in energy and less stable than orbitals with a single electron.

The *octet rule* refers to atoms' tendency to gain, lose or share electrons to achieve a full orbital of eight electrons in its *valence* (i.e., outermost) orbital. The octet rule only applies to the *s* and *p* orbital electrons. Therefore, the octet rule is particularly useful when applied to the *representative elements.* Representative elements are not in the transition block (*d* orbitals) or the inner-transition metal block (*f* orbitals, known as *lanthanides* and *actinides*). A complete octet is typically represented as an electron configuration ending in s^2p^6. When atoms have either an excess or deficiency in the number of valence (outermost) electrons, they react to satisfy their octets and form more stable compounds.

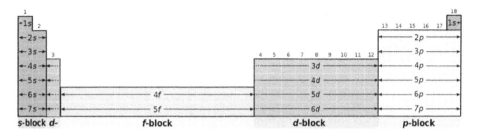

The vertical columns are groups (families). The representative elements are the left two groups with s shells (metals) and six right p orbitals (nonmetals).

Using the Aufbau Principle and Hund's Rule, the electron configuration for zinc (Zn) atom with 30 electrons is:

$$1s^2 \; 2s^2 \; 2p^6 \; 3s^2 \; 3p^6 \; 4s^2 \; 3d^{10}$$

- The first number indicates the principal energy level (n).

- The letter (s, p, d, f) indicates the subshell (which ranges from 0 to $n-1$).

- The superscript indicates the number of electrons in the subshell.

As the number of electrons in an atom increases across the periodic table, the electron configurations become exceedingly long.

There is a shorthand approach to writing electron configurations that reference the noble gases (or inert gases). The noble gases have complete octets and are located in the far-right column (group or family) of the periodic table (Group 18).

The electronic configurations of Na (atomic number or Z is 11):

1. Identify the noble gas that comes before the element in the periodic table (i.e., the noble gas in the previous row, also called *periods*).

    The noble gas before Na ($Z = 11$) is Ne ($Z = 10$)

    The noble gas before Cl ($Z = 17$) is Ne ($Z = 10$), not Ar ($Z = 18$)

2. Write the noble gas in square brackets:

    [Ne]

    Ne has the electron configuration of $1s^2 2s^2 2p^6$

3. Write the electron configuration for Na:

    Na: $1s^2 2s^2 2p^6 3s^1$

4. Abbreviate the electron configuration by referencing Ne:

    [Ne] $3s^1$

Example: the electronic configurations of Zn (atomic number or Z is 30):

Zinc: $1s^2 2s^2 2p^6 3s^2 3p^6 4s^2 3d^{10}$

The noble gas argon has a Z value $= 18$

The short-hand electronic configuration for Zn is:

[Ar] $4s^2 3d^{10}$

When writing electron configurations for ions of an element, add or subtract the number of electrons gained or lost from the atom when filling the subshells ($s. p, d, f$).

For sodium (Na), the electron configuration is:

Na: $1s^2 2s^2 2p^6 3s^1$

However, when sodium reacts to form the Na^+ cation, it loses one electron, and its electron configuration becomes:

Na^+: $1s^2 2s^2 2p^6$

Notice that the electron configuration for the sodium cation is identical to Ne because both have 10 electrons.

When writing electron configurations, there are a few exceptions to the guidelines above because of the *stability rule*. The stability rule states that a sublevel is more stable when it has a half-filled configuration (one electron in every orbital) or a full configuration (two electrons in every orbital).

If an atom is only one short of achieving a half-filled or full configuration, it takes an electron from a neighboring s orbital to increase its stability. This promoting of an electron from the s orbital is most commonly seen with the transition metals.

Chromium (Cr, 24 electrons) has the electron configuration:

$$[Ar]\ 4s^2 3d^4$$

According to the stability rule, the Cr electron configuration is more stable with a half-filled configuration:

$$[Ar]\ 4s^1 3d^5$$

The $3d$ subshell took an electron from the neighboring $4s$ subshell. The $4s$ subshell now has a partially filled orbital.

Copper (Cu) has 29 electrons with the expected electron configuration:

$$[Ar]\ 4s^2 3d^9$$

From the stability rule, the electron configuration changes to the more stable:

$$[Ar]\ 4s^1 3d^{10}$$

The $3d$ subshell of Cu has the electron configuration of $4s^1$, which is now partially filled.

An *orbital diagram* is another way to express an atom's electron configuration. Orbital diagrams are a visual representation that uses fishhook (single-headed) arrows to indicate electrons in orbitals, as shown on the left side below.

$\underset{1s}{\uparrow\downarrow}\ \underset{2s}{\uparrow\downarrow}\ \underset{2px}{\uparrow}\ \underset{2py}{\uparrow}\ \underset{2pz}{\_\_}$	$1s^2\,2s^2\,2p^2$
Single-headed fishhook arrow points up or down to represent an electron. Each line horizontal represents an orbital; the subshell and energy level are written below the line. Spaces separate the subshells *there are three horizontal lines for the three p orbitals (x, y, z)	Coefficient = energy level (1, 2) Letter = subshell (s, p) Exponent = # of electrons in subshell This method does not give as much information as orbital diagrams.

Bohr atom

It is vital to understand the scientific discoveries that contributed to the current model of the atom. At the beginning of the 19th century, chemists were able to show that pure compounds contained fixed and unvarying amounts of their constituent components.

In 1806, John Dalton (1766-1844) provided a significant step in explaining this model of an atom with his particle theory, known as *Dalton's Atomic Theory.*

Dalton's Atomic Theory consisted of these essential principles:

1. All matter is composed of microscopic particles, known as atoms.

2. Atoms of one element have the same shape, size, mass, and other properties. Atoms of an element differ in properties from atoms of other elements.

3. Atoms can neither be subdivided nor changed into another atom.

4. Atoms cannot be created nor destroyed.

5. The atom is the smallest unit of matter that undergoes a chemical reaction.

In addition to these principles, Dalton proposed the "*rule of greatest simplicity,*" which suggested that atoms only combine in binary ratios (i.e., 1:1). This rule was problematic because Dalton assumed that the formula for water was HO instead of H_2O.

Dalton eventually suggested that the rule of greatest simplicity was not correct, and in 1810, he suggested that a water molecule has three atoms. Atoms combine in whole-number ratios (1:1, 1:2, 1:3, ...) following the "*law of multiple proportions.*"

There are problems with Dalton's Atomic Theory. He claimed that all atoms of an element have the same mass. The discovery of isotopes, which are atoms of the same element that vary in mass and density (different number of neutrons), proves otherwise.

Additionally, it is now known that atoms can be subdivided into their constituent particles in nuclear processes; Dalton's postulate that atoms cannot be subdivided remains correct within the scope of chemical reactions.

In the early 1900s, German Nobel laureate physicists Max Planck (1858-1947) discovered that radiation is emitted in quantized amounts of energy instead of a single continuous ray.

Based on Planck's discovery, Nobel laureate Niels Bohr (1885-1962) conducted experiments on hydrogen atoms and revised the atom model. Bohr suggested that electrons orbit the nucleus in fixed orbits with defined energies and sizes. Bohr's model is like how planets orbit the sun (except that the attraction within the atom is provided by electrostatic forces rather than gravity). When electrons transition between orbits, they emit or absorb energy equivalent to the difference in energy levels between the orbits.

Bohr identified each energy level using an integer n, known as the principal quantum number. Bohr also determined that additional electrons always occupy the lowest available energy level.

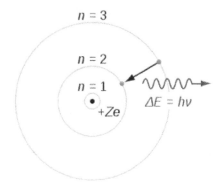

Bohr's model of electrons in discrete orbitals according to specific energy levels

Quantum numbers l, m_l and m_s and the number of electrons per orbital; Pauli Exclusion Principle

The *azimuthal quantum number* or *angular momentum quantum number* (l) is the second quantum number that defines the *shape* of an orbital. Except for the first level where $n = 1$, the principal energy levels have two or more possible subshells (s, p, d, f) with different energy levels.

For any n, the values for the azimuthal (angular momentum) quantum number l may range from 0 to ($n - 1$). The number of subshells for any given energy level is equal to the value of n and is represented by the letters $s, p, d,$ and f.

Orbital	Angular Momentum Quantum Number
s	$l = 0$
p	$l = 1$
d	$l = 2$
f	$l = 3$

The *magnetic quantum number* (m_l) is the third quantum number that describes the *orientation* of an orbital. The magnetic quantum number defines the number of orbitals within a subshell.

The possible values for m_l range from $-l$ to $+l$, including 0.

- An *s* subshell has $l = 0$, the m_l has only a single value (0), and it only has one orbital

  A *s* subshell can hold 2 electrons.

- A *p* subshell has $l = 1$, the m_l can have the values of −1, 0, +1.

  A *p* subshell has three orbitals and can hold up to 6 electrons.

- A *d* subshell has $l = 2$, the $m_l = -2, -1, 0, +1, +2$.

  A *d* subshell has five orbitals and can hold up to 10 electrons.

- An *f* subshell has $l = 3$, the $m_l = -3, -2, -1, 0, +1, +2, +3$.

  An *f* subshell has seven orbitals and can hold up to 14 electrons.

Each successive subshell holds 4 more electrons than its predecessor.

The *spin quantum number* (m_s) is the fourth quantum number and describes the electron spin of an individual electron that occupies an orbital.

The spin quantum number distinguishes specific electrons within an orbital.

There are two opposing values for electron-spin: $+\frac{1}{2}$ and $-\frac{1}{2}$.

By convention, the first electron to occupy an orbital has a spin number of $+\frac{1}{2}$ while the second electron has a spin number of $-\frac{1}{2}$.

In orbital diagrams, the $+\frac{1}{2}$ electrons are represented by upward arrows, and the $-\frac{1}{2}$ electrons are indicated by downward arrows.

Energy Level	Number of subshells	Subshells	# of orbitals in that subshell	Total number of electrons in a subshell
1	1	*s*	1	2
2	2	*s*	1	2
		p	3	6
3	3	*s*	1	2
		p	3	6
		d	5	10
4	4	*s*	1	2
		p	3	6
		d	5	10
		f	7	14

Quantum numbers represent the locations of the electrons within the atom

In 1925, Nobel laureate Wolfgang Pauli (1900-1958) proposed the *Pauli Exclusion Principle,* which states that no two electrons in the same atom may have the same four quantum numbers (n, l, m_l and m_s).

The maximum number of electrons in an orbital is two, and they must possess opposite spins ($+\frac{1}{2}$ or $-\frac{1}{2}$) because electrons of the same magnetic spin cannot both be in the same subshell of an orbital.

Common names and geometric shapes for orbitals: *s, p, d, f*

There are four types of orbitals whose shapes were predicted using wave mechanics (described below).

The four types of orbitals are *s, p, d,* and *f* from the initial letters of the words **s**harp, **p**rincipal, **d**iffuse, and **f**undamental. Each energy level has between 1 and 4 subshells. Each subshell is associated with an electron probability density of a shape.

Each subshell has a specific number of orbitals as given by the m_l value.

- *s orbitals* are spheres:

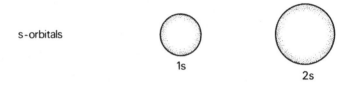

p orbitals have two lobes and are dumbbell-shaped. There are three different p orbitals (three orientations: p_x, p_y, p_z):

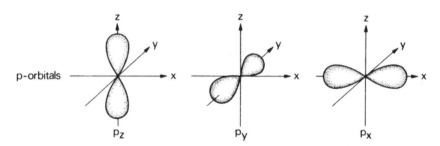

- *d orbitals have four lobes and are clover shaped. There are five different d orbitals (five orientations: d_{yz}, d_{z}^{2}, d_{xy}, d_{xz}, $d_{x-y}^{2\ 2}$):*

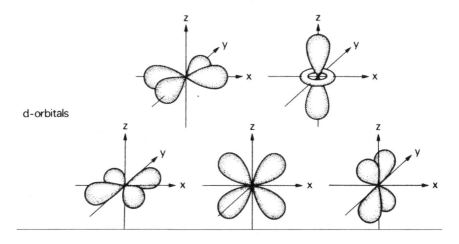

d-orbitals

- *f orbitals are complicated, and the shape is a combination of the shapes of the other orbitals. There are seven f orbitals:*

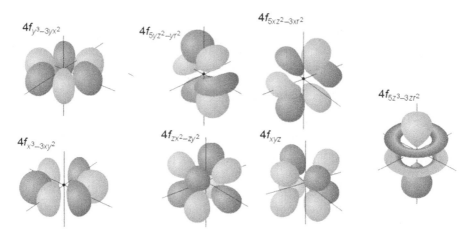

Heisenberg uncertainty principle

A series of remarkable discoveries led to quantum mechanics and enabled an evolved model to understand electron behavior.

In 1924, Nobel laureate Louis de Broglie (1892-1987) published his work on *wave-particle duality*. He proposed that electrons could be classified as both *particles* and *waves* simultaneously. Louis de Broglie proposed that electrons are particles with mass and velocity but also possess *wave properties* such as wavelength and frequency.

The de Broglie equation demonstrates that all objects exhibit wave-behavior. However, the wave-behavior of everyday objects becomes negligible as the mass increases. Subatomic particles have tiny masses:

$$\lambda = h \,/\, mv$$

where λ is the wavelength, m is the mass, h is Planck's constant (6.626×10^{-34} J·s), and v is the velocity.

In 1926, Nobel laureate Erwin Schrödinger (1887-1961) derived a wave equation that models the movement of electrons based on their wave properties. In quantum mechanics, the solution to Schrödinger's wave equation yields a *wave function*, represented by the uppercase Greek letter psi (Ψ), which, by itself, does not indicate much about the atom. However, the square of the absolute value of psi, $|\Psi|^2$ gives the *probability density* of an electron's position.

The wave function $|\Psi(x)|^2$ gives the probability of locating an electron at position x. Orbitals are electron "*clouds*" because they represent the probability of an electron's specific location in the atom. Schrödinger's equation showed that electrons behave like waves. It implies that electrons do not travel in clearly defined paths and that it is impossible to determine an electron's exact position and speed.

German physicist Nobel laureate Werner Heisenberg (1901-1976) developed a theory based on the premise that there is a theoretical limit to how small the uncertainty in the measurements can be.

The *Heisenberg Uncertainty Principle* states that both the position and momentum of an electron cannot be measured simultaneously at any point in time. The measurement of position or momentum distorts the value for the other.

Heisenberg Uncertainty Principle is expressed as:

$$\Delta x \times \Delta p \geq \frac{h}{4\pi}$$

where Δx is the *uncertainty in position*, Δp is the *uncertainty in momentum*, and h is Planck's constant of 6.626×10^{-34} J·s.

Paramagnetism and diamagnetism

Electrons are constantly spinning in a fixed direction, which generates magnetic fields. According to the Pauli Exclusion Principle, if one electron is spinning in a clockwise direction, the other electron must be spinning in a counterclockwise direction. These opposing spins result in the orbital having no net spin.

Since electrons occupying the same orbital always have opposite values for their spin quantum numbers (m_s), they always have different sets of quantum numbers.

Atoms can be classified based on their electron-induced magnetic behavior as ferromagnetic, diamagnetic, or paramagnetic.

1. *Diamagnetic* materials generate an induced magnetic field in a direction opposite to an externally applied magnetic field. The applied magnetic field repels these materials.

   All electrons in diamagnetic atoms are paired.

2. *Paramagnetic* materials, when in the presence of a magnetic field, generate internally-induced magnetic fields in the same direction as the external field. A paramagnetic electron is an unpaired electron. An atom is paramagnetic if it has at least one unpaired paramagnetic electron in any orbital, regardless of the number of paired electrons.

   Paramagnetic atoms are slightly attracted to a magnetic field and cannot retain magnetization without an external magnetic field.

3. *Ferromagnetic* materials generate permanent magnetic moments without needing an applied external magnetic field. Certain transition metals, such as iron and nickel, have ferromagnetic properties.

   Electrons of ferromagnetic substances can spontaneously align themselves in the same direction, reinforcing each electron's magnetic properties.

Photoelectric effect

In 1905, Albert Einstein (1879-1955) proposed the *photoelectric effect* that explained how incoming visible light interacts with electrons when light is reflected off the surfaces of metals. Discrete packets of light energy, known as *photons*, are transferred to electrons on a metal surface as kinetic energy.

When electrons possess sufficient energy to escape, *emission* of electrons from the metal may occur. The emission of electrons only occurs if the incident light possesses energy greater than or equal to the *work function* ϕ_w of the electron.

Energy (E) of light waves is calculated by the formula:

$$E = h\nu$$

where h is Planck's constant and ν is the frequency of the light wave (Hz)

Einstein's model for the photoelectric effect accurately predicts that a photon's energy is proportional to its frequency and not its intensity.

Ground state, excited states

Every electron in an atom occupies a fixed orbital. When an electron occupies its default orbital, the electron is in its *ground state*. A ground-state electron is at its lowest energy level and is the most stable. If an electron absorbs energy, it has greater potential energy and occupies a higher energy level. An electron in a higher energy level is known as an *excited state* electron. An electron can remain in its excited state for a limited time before it drops back to its ground state and emits the excess energy as visible electromagnetic radiation.

Absorption and emission spectra

Electrons can only move between fixed orbitals, which means that the wavelength of light released or absorbed when they transition between energy levels is limited to a specific set of visible wavelengths known as the *line spectrum*.

A line spectrum is produced by gas under low pressure. Solids, liquids, and compressed gases produce *continuous spectra*, which contain all the colors of visible light.

Different elements have different numbers of electrons, which means that each element has a unique set of *atomic emission spectra* represented by discrete lines along a frequency scale. Due to the uniqueness of this chemical property, *the atomic emission spectra can* be used to identify elements in a mixture.

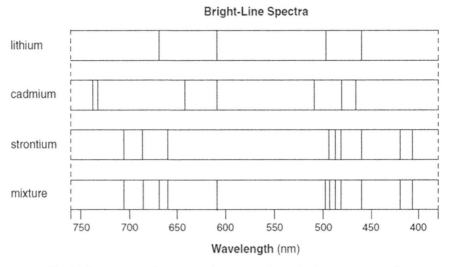

Each element produces a unique atomic emission spectrum that permits the classification of elements within a mixture

The *atomic absorption spectra* indicate the amount of energy absorbed when electrons are promoted to orbitals with higher energy levels.

An element's absorption and emission spectrum correlate because the net difference between energy levels will be the same, regardless of the direction of the electron's movement.

The atomic emission spectrum of hydrogen has been widely observed. Its spectrum consists of five series of lines, and each series is named after its discoverer. Lyman ($n = 1$), Balmer ($n = 2$), Paschen ($n = 3$), Brackett ($n = 4$), Pfund ($n = 5$) and Humphreys ($n = 6$). The most important emission series are the *Lyman, Balmer,* and *Paschen* series, which correspond to *ultraviolet, visible,* and *infrared* radiation, respectively.

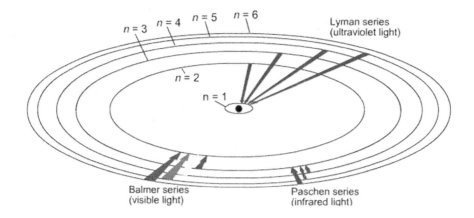

Atomic emission spectrum for a hydrogen atom

Swedish physicist Johannes Rydberg (1854-1919) proposed an equation describing the relationship between spectral lines of different elements.

The *Rydberg formula* for hydrogen, which calculates the energy emission of hydrogen electrons, is expressed as:

$E = hc / \lambda$

$$E = -R_h \left[\frac{1}{(n_i)^2} - \frac{1}{(n_f)^2} \right]$$

where R_h is Rydberg's constant (2.179×10^{-18} J), n_i is the principal quantum number of the initial orbital, n_f is the principal quantum number of the final orbital, c is the speed of light (3.0×10^8 m/s), λ is the wavelength and h is Planck's constant (6.626×10^{-34} J·s).

Chemical Properties Variations with Group and Row

After the discovery of several new elements in the 18th and 19th centuries, scientists noticed that elements could be categorized into groups with similar properties. In 1869, the first significant development for this observation occurred when Russian chemist Dimitri Mendeleev (1834-1907) and German chemist Julius Lothar Meyer (1830-1895) independently published variations for the periodic table.

Mendeleev arranged the elements by their atomic masses, which resulted in the similarity of physical and chemical properties between elements in the same column or group. Mendeleev's table was revolutionary because it accurately predicted the position of undiscovered elements. Meyer arranged his table based on increasing atomic volume.

Although Mendeleev's table exhibited patterns of similarities between elements in the same column or group, there were some exceptions. For example, argon exists in elemental form as an unreactive gas (noble gas or inert gas), but it was categorized with the highly reactive sodium and lithium metals.

In 1913, British physicist Henry Moseley (1887-1915) improved Mendeleev's periodic table by proposing that the chemical properties of elements are related to their atomic number (Z, number of protons) instead of their atomic weight (A, number of protons and neutrons). Moseley's discovery became the foundation of the modern periodic table.

The modern periodic table arranges elements in rows and columns.

The horizontal rows are *periods*, identified by numbers (1-7).

The vertical columns are *groups* or *families* (1-18).

There are different standards for group nomenclature:

- In the older system, each group was assigned a Roman numeral (I-VIII) based on the number of valence electrons.

- The groups were also assigned a letter (A or B) based on their location on the table. However, there were two different standards on the A/B designation. The American standard assigned A to the main (representative) group of elements on the sides and B to the transition group in the center.

- The European standard assigned A to the left side and B to the right side of the table.

- For consistency, a new universal naming standard was devised from left to right; the groups are given consecutive integers (1-18).

Elements are ordered by increasing atomic number, so there are recurring properties within the rows (periods) and columns (groups or families). Several physical and chemical properties of elements can be predicted from their position in the periodic table. These periodic trends include the number of valence (outermost) electrons, ionization energy, electron affinity, atomic or ionic radii, and electronegativity.

Valence electrons

Valence electrons are the outermost shell electrons and are responsible for the formation of chemical bonds. The group numbers represent the number of valence electrons for elements in the column on the periodic table. However, this rule only applies to the main group elements and does not apply to the transition metals.

Two factors contribute to valence electrons experiencing weaker electrostatic attraction from the protons in the nucleus. The first is the distance of the electron n shell from the nucleus. The increased distance of higher principal quantum numbers for the electron's orbital increased the distance from the nucleus and decreased attraction.

Coulomb's Law expresses electrostatic force:

$$F = kq_1q_2 / r^2$$

where F is the electrostatic force, k is Coulomb's constant (9×10^9 N·m^2/C^2), q_1 and q_2 are the respective charges of the two particles, and r is the distance between the particles.

The second factor is *screening electrons*, which are inner electrons that shield the attractive force experienced by the valence electrons.

Periodic Table of the Elements

Legend
Atomic Number / Valence
Symbol
Name / Atomic Mass

1 IA 1A	2 IIA 2A	3 IIIB 3B	4 IVB 4B	5 VB 5B	6 VIB 6B	7 VIIB 7B	8 VIII 8	9 VIII 8	10 VIII 8	11 IB 1B	12 IIB 2B	13 IIIA 3A	14 IVA 4A	15 VA 5A	16 VIA 6A	17 VIIA 7A	18 VIIIA 8A
1 -1,+1 **H** Hydrogen 1.008																	2 0 **He** Helium 4.003
3 +1 **Li** Lithium 6.941	4 +2 **Be** Beryllium 9.012											5 +3 **B** Boron 10.811	6 +4,+3,+2,±1 **C** Carbon 12.011	7 +5,-3 **N** Nitrogen 14.007	8 -2 **O** Oxygen 15.999	9 -1 **F** Fluorine 18.998	10 0 **Ne** Neon 20.180
11 +1 **Na** Sodium 22.990	12 +2 **Mg** Magnesium 24.305											13 +3 **Al** Aluminum 26.982	14 +4 **Si** Silicon 28.086	15 +5,-3,3 **P** Phosphorus 30.974	16 +6,+4,-2,2 **S** Sulfur 32.066	17 +7,+5,+3,+1,-1 **Cl** Chlorine 35.453	18 0 **Ar** Argon 39.948
19 +1 **K** Potassium 39.098	20 +2 **Ca** Calcium 40.078	21 +3 **Sc** Scandium 44.956	22 +4 **Ti** Titanium 47.88	23 +5 **V** Vanadium 50.942	24 +3 **Cr** Chromium 51.996	25 +7,+4,+2 **Mn** Manganese 54.938	26 +6,-3,+2 **Fe** Iron 55.845	27 +3,+2 **Co** Cobalt 58.933	28 +2 **Ni** Nickel 58.693	29 +2 **Cu** Copper 63.546	30 +2 **Zn** Zinc 65.38	31 +3 **Ga** Gallium 69.723	32 +4,+2,-4 **Ge** Germanium 72.631	33 +5,+3,-3 **As** Arsenic 74.922	34 +6,+4,-2,2 **Se** Selenium 78.971	35 +5,+3,+1,-1 **Br** Bromine 79.904	36 0 **Kr** Krypton 84.798
37 +1 **Rb** Rubidium 85.468	38 +2 **Sr** Strontium 87.62	39 +3 **Y** Yttrium 88.906	40 +4 **Zr** Zirconium 91.224	41 +5 **Nb** Niobium 92.906	42 +6,+4 **Mo** Molybdenum 95.95	43 +7,-4 **Tc** Technetium 98.907	44 +4,+3 **Ru** Ruthenium 101.07	45 +3,+2 **Rh** Rhodium 102.906	46 +4,+2 **Pd** Palladium 106.42	47 +3 **Ag** Silver 107.868	48 +2 **Cd** Cadmium 112.414	49 +3 **In** Indium 114.818	50 +4,+2 **Sn** Tin 118.711	51 +5,+3,-3 **Sb** Antimony 121.760	52 +6,+4,-2,2 **Te** Tellurium 127.6	53 +7,+5,+3,+1,-1 **I** Iodine 126.904	54 +6,+4,+2,0 **Xe** Xenon 131.294
55 +1 **Cs** Cesium 132.905	56 +2 **Ba** Barium 137.328	57-71	72 +4 **Hf** Hafnium 178.49	73 +5 **Ta** Tantalum 180.948	74 +6 **W** Tungsten 183.85	75 +7 **Re** Rhenium 186.207	76 +8 **Os** Osmium 190.23	77 +4,+3 **Ir** Iridium 192.22	78 +4,+2 **Pt** Platinum 195.08	79 +3 **Au** Gold 196.967	80 +2,+1 **Hg** Mercury 200.59	81 +3,+1 **Tl** Thallium 204.383	82 +4,+2 **Pb** Lead 207.2	83 +3 **Bi** Bismuth 208.980	84 +4,+2,-2 **Po** Polonium [208.982]	85 +1,-1 **At** Astatine 209.987	86 0 **Rn** Radon 222.018
87 +1 **Fr** Francium 223.020	88 +2 **Ra** Radium 226.025	89-103	104 unknown **Rf** Rutherfordium [261]	105 unknown **Db** Dubnium [262]	106 unknown **Sg** Seaborgium [266]	107 unknown **Bh** Bohrium [264]	108 unknown **Hs** Hassium [269]	109 unknown **Mt** Meitnerium [278]	110 unknown **Ds** Darmstadtium [281]	111 unknown **Rg** Roentgenium [280]	112 unknown **Cn** Copernicium [285]	113 unknown **Nh** Nihonium [286]	114 unknown **Fl** Flerovium [289]	115 unknown **Mc** Moscovium [289]	116 unknown **Lv** Livermorium [293]	117 unknown **Ts** Tennessine [294]	118 unknown **Og** Oganesson [294]

Lanthanide Series

57 +3 **La** Lanthanum 138.905	58 +4,+3 **Ce** Cerium 140.116	59 +3 **Pr** Praseodymium 140.908	60 +3 **Nd** Neodymium 144.243	61 +3 **Pm** Promethium 144.913	62 +3 **Sm** Samarium 150.36	63 +3 **Eu** Europium 151.964	64 +3 **Gd** Gadolinium 157.25	65 +3 **Tb** Terbium 158.925	66 +3 **Dy** Dysprosium 162.500	67 +3 **Ho** Holmium 164.930	68 +3 **Er** Erbium 167.259	69 +3 **Tm** Thulium 168.934	70 +3 **Yb** Ytterbium 173.055	71 +3 **Lu** Lutetium 174.967

Actinide Series

89 +3 **Ac** Actinium 227.028	90 +4 **Th** Thorium 232.038	91 +5 **Pa** Protactinium 231.036	92 +6 **U** Uranium 238.029	93 +5 **Np** Neptunium 237.048	94 +4 **Pu** Plutonium 244.064	95 +3 **Am** Americium 243.061	96 +3 **Cm** Curium 247.070	97 +3 **Bk** Berkelium 247.070	98 +3 **Cf** Californium 251.080	99 +3 **Es** Einsteinium [254]	100 +3 **Fm** Fermium 257.095	101 +2 **Md** Mendelevium 258.1	102 +2 **No** Nobelium 259.101	103 +3 **Lr** Lawrencium [262]

Effective nuclear charge

The *nuclear charge* is the charge of the positive protons in the nucleus, and it describes the extent to which electrons are pulled toward the nucleus.

The *effective nuclear charge* (Z_{eff}) is the net nuclear force experienced by valence electrons after accounting for electron shielding by inner orbital electrons.

The *effective nuclear charge* is calculated by:

$$Z_{eff} = Z - S$$

where Z is the number of protons in the nucleus (i.e., the atomic number), and S is the average number of screening electrons between the nucleus and the valence electron.

The effective nuclear charge experienced by an electron is proportional to its stability: the more stable the electron, the higher the effective nuclear charge, and the more energy is required to remove the electron; ionization energy

Effective nuclear charge increases across a period due to increasing nuclear charge (increasing number of protons) but no accompanying increase in shielding effect.

There is no general trend down a group because both the nuclear charge (Z) and shielding effect increase as more electron shells are added.

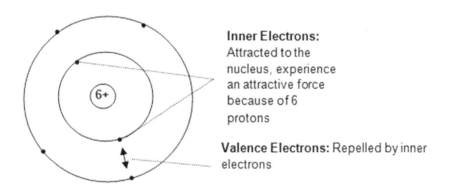

Inner Electrons: Attracted to the nucleus, experience an attractive force because of 6 protons

Valence Electrons: Repelled by inner electrons

Effective Nuclear Charge:
valence electrons only "feel" an attractive force of 4 protons.
The two inner electrons cancel the +2 of the nuclear charge due to shielding.

First and second ionization energy

The *ionization energy* (SI Units kJ/mol) is the energy required to remove an electron from a neutral atom of an element or an ion in the gaseous state. The ionization of an electron requires energy and is an endothermic process (i.e., it absorbs heat).

While electrons are removed from the atom, the number of protons in the nucleus is constant. Therefore, the remaining electrons experience a stronger electrostatic force, as the constant force from the nucleus is shared among fewer remaining electrons.

Ionization energies increase for each successive removal of an electron due to the increase in electrostatic force. Thus, the first electron is the easiest to remove.

The *first ionization energy* is the energy needed to remove an outermost electron.

The *second ionization energy* is the energy needed to remove a second electron.

Low ionization energy indicates that an electron is easily lost. This property is most commonly found in metals, with the Group I elements (alkali metal) having the lowest IE values. Conversely, high IE indicates that an electron is not easily removed. High ionization energy is mostly associated with nonmetals because of their natural tendency to gain electrons to form anions instead of losing electrons. The highest values are found for the inert gases (Group 8 or VIII) because they have octets, making them extremely stable.

A more substantial positive nuclear charge results in a stronger electrostatic attraction and higher ionization energy for the valence electrons. In contrast, a larger atomic radius means that the outermost electrons are further from the nucleus and have a weaker electrostatic attraction, increased shielding, and lower ionization energy.

If an electron is in a lower shell (closer to the nucleus), it has lower energy and is more difficult to dislodge. Thus, it has higher ionization energy and requires more energy for the electron to be abstracted from the atom.

Half-filled shells are exceptions to the trend for ionization energy because these configurations are more stable than filled shell configurations. Half-filled shells occur when an atom's valence *p* or *d* orbital is half-filled (one electron in every subshell).

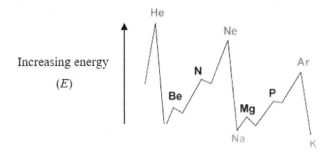

A complete octet (filled s and p subshells) increases the stability of the electrons

Ionization energies generally increase from left to right across a given period due to the atom's increased effective nuclear charge. At the same time, the shielding effect due to the number of inner electron shells remains constant.

Ionization energies generally decrease from top to bottom down a group due to the increasing distance from the nucleus corresponding to the increased principal quantum number n and the shielding effect of the electrons in the inner shells.

The ionization energy decreases down a group because of the increasing distance for the valence electrons to the nucleus and the increase in shielding by more shells of inner electrons. The graph's highest peaks are noble gases (stable due to filled octets), while the lowest valleys are alkali metals with single valence electrons in the valence shell. Local maxima occur for filled subshells and half-filled p subshells.

Electron affinity

Electron affinity is the energy released when an electron adds to a neutral atom. As the name implies, elements with high electron affinity are strongly attracted to electrons and are associated with exothermic reactions (i.e., reactions that release heat). Electron affinity for nonmetals is indicative of their tendency to gain electrons and form negatively charged anions (Cl⁻ or Br⁻).

The first electron affinity is the energy released when one electron adds; it is *exothermic* and releases heat.

The second electron affinity is *endothermic* because adding an electron to an orbital with excess electrons results in repulsion; thus, energy must be added to overcome the electrostatic repulsions among electrons and stabilize the additional electron.

The elements that prefer electrons most are the nonmetals, which have the highest electron affinities. The elements that do not prefer extra electrons are the metals, which have low electron affinities.

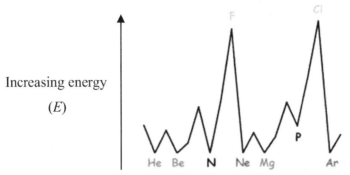

Electron affinity is highest for F, and Cl which results in complete p subshells

On the electron affinity graph, the highest peaks are for the halogens (F. Cl. Br, I, At), and the lowest peaks are for noble gases (e.g., Ne. Ar, Kr).

Local minima in energy occurs for filled subshells and half-filled *p* subshells; this is observed for the noble gases of neon (Ne) and argon (Ar).

Like ionization energy, electron affinity is a periodic trend that generally increases from left to right and decreases from top to bottom (except the noble gases).

Electronegativity

In 1932, American chemist Nobel laureate Linus Pauling (1901-1994) derived a set of elemental values based on ionization energies (tendency to lose electrons) and electron affinities (tendency to gain electrons).

Electronegativity is the element's tendency to gain bonding electrons. Electronegativity is the measure of an atom's attraction for the electrons in a bond with another atom. On the Pauling scale, electronegativity values range from a low of 0.7 (Fr) to a high of 4.0 (F).

From the periodic table below, electronegativity values generally increase from left to right and decrease from top to bottom on the periodic table. The most electronegative elements are at the top right corner of the periodic table. The least electronegative (i.e., most electropositive) elements are in the bottom left corner. Therefore, nonmetals are typically more electronegative than metals. There are no electronegativity values given for the noble gases because they usually do not bond with other elements.

In general, these electronegativity trends can be explained similarly to ionization energy and electron affinity: as the atomic number increases, the positive nuclear charge increases, and the electrons within the same energy level (same shielding effect) are more strongly attracted to the positive nucleus.

H 2.1																	
Li 1.0	Be 1.5												B 1.5	C 2.5	N 3.0	D 3.5	F 4.0
Na 0.9	Mg 1.2												Al 1.5	Si 1.8	P 2.1	S 3.5	Cl 3.0
K 0.8	Ca 1.0	Sc 1.3	Ti 1.5	V 1.6	Cr 1.6	Mn 1.5	Fe 1.8	Co 1.9	Ni 1.8	Cu 1.9	Zn 1.6	Ga 1.6	Ge 1.8	As 2.0	Se 2.4	Br 2.8
Rb 0.8	Sr 1.0	Y 1.2	Zr 1.4	Nb 1.6	Mo 1.8	Tc 1.9	Ru 2.2	Rh 2.2	Pd 2.2	Ag 1.9	Cd 1.7	In 1.7	Sn 1.8	Sb 1.9	Te 2.1	I 2.5
Cs 0.7	Ba 0.9		Hf 1.3	Ta 1.5	W 1.7	Re 1.9	Os 2.2	Ir 2.2	Pt 2.2	Au 2.4	Hg 1.9	Tl 1.8	Pb 1.9	Bi 1.9	Po 2.0	At 2.2
Fr 0.7	Ra 0.9															

Pauling's electronegativity values assigned to elements on the periodic table

A *covalent bond* is the relatively equal sharing of electrons between two elements. If the electronegativity of the two atoms is the same (or similar), they share the electrons equally (or almost equally).

A *polar covalent bond* results if there is a sufficient difference in electronegativity between the atoms (see the table below for value ranges). In a polar covalent bond, the more electronegative element has a greater tendency to attract electrons. This atom gets a larger share of the electron density, giving it a partial negative (δ^-) charge. The less electronegative element in a polar covalent bond has a weaker tendency to attract electrons. The atom gets a smaller share of the electron density, giving it a partial positive (δ^+) charge.

An *ionic bond* occurs if the electronegativity difference is significant (see the table below). Ionic bonds transfer an electron from the electropositive element to the electronegative element. Ionic bonds generally occur between a metal (left two columns; groups 1 and 2) and a nonmetal (right side; generally, groups 16 and 17).

The difference in electronegativity between atoms participating in a bond is the *dipole moment* and measured in units of *debye* (*D*). Based on electronegativity, bonds are classified as covalent, polar covalent, or ionic.

Type of Bond	Dipole Moment (*D*)
Covalent	$0 - 0.6$
Polar covalent	$0.6 - 1.6$
Ionic bonds	> 1.6

Electron shells and the sizes of atoms

Electron shells are defined by the principal quantum number n. With an increasing atomic number, elements have more electrons and, therefore, more electron shells.

From top to bottom down a group, the shielding effect increases because the closer shells are between the nucleus and the outermost shell.

Extra shells increase the atom size because of a new orbit (i.e., higher shells have a more considerable distance from the nucleus than lower shells).

For elements left to right across a row on the periodic table, the principal quantum number n is the same; therefore, the same shell fills with the additional electrons. As a shell fills, the effective nuclear charge increases because of the increasing number of protons, while additional electrons fill the same orbit and no increase in shielding. With the increasing effective nuclear charge, the electrostatic attraction between the nucleus and the electrons increases, so the atom becomes more compact.

Atomic radius is ½ the distance between the two atomic nuclei and measures the sizes of atoms since electron clouds are too ill-defined to measure precisely.

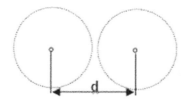

The atomic radii measure the distance between the atomic nuclei of two atoms

The trends in relative atomic radii in periods 2 and 3 are illustrated below.

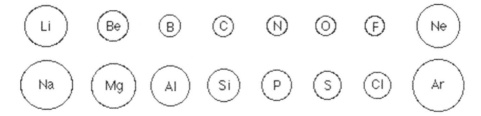

On a relative scale, if a nucleus were the size of a ping-pong ball, the atom's diameter would be 25 miles. Therefore, an increase in the size of the nucleus does not substantially affect the overall size of an atom.

From top to bottom down a group on the periodic table, the atoms become larger because electrons add to new orbitals farther from the nucleus.

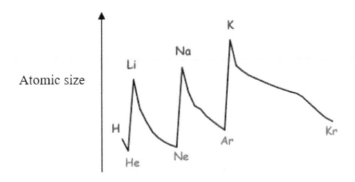

Atomic radii trend increases
as the principal number increases for additional orbitals

The peaks on the energy *vs.* atomic number graph represent atoms with a single electron in the valence shell, while the valleys are for atoms with a filled valence shell.

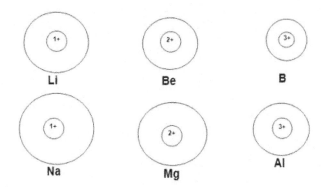

The relative size of the electron shells is indicated across a group and down periods. The nucleus is shown at the center and the corresponding 1s orbital for the ions (Li and Na are 1+; Be and Mg are 2+; B and Al are 3+). Across the group, the effective nuclear charge increases with the addition of protons (increasing Z value) in the nucleus.

An atom's size increases down a column due to an increasing number of shells (*n* number) and decreases across a row due to the increased nuclear attraction (higher number of nuclear core protons).

Notes

Notes

Notes

Classification of Elements into Groups by Electronic Structure; Physical and Chemical Properties of Elements

The vertical columns (groups or families) of the periodic table have recurring trends. For this reason, some of the groups are given unique names, sometimes referred to as common names or *unsystematic names* (e.g., alkali metals). Elements in the same group have the same number of valence electrons and tend to show patterns in physical properties such as ionization energy, atomic radius, and electronegativity.

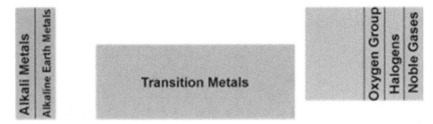

Sample common names for groups on the periodic table

The periodic table can be divided into blocks based on the subshell (*s*, *p*, *d*, *f* orbitals) in which the valence (outermost) electron is located.

In some blocks, the horizontal trends are especially important.

The four blocks are the *s*-block, the *p*-block, the *d*-block, and the *f*-block. These blocks are seen in the figure below, indicating the principal quantum number *n* and the azimuthal quantum number *l* for the subshells *s*, *p*, *d*, and *f* are shown in the figure. The *f*-block (i.e., lanthanides and actinides) is generally displayed separately below the periodic table.

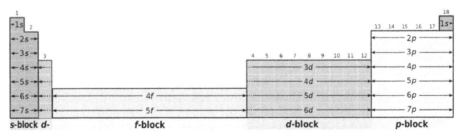

Representative elements

The representative (or main-group) elements (Groups 1, 2 and 13-18) comprise the *s* (1-2) and *p*-blocks (13-18), and their properties are as follows:

- No free-flowing (or loosely bound) outer *d* electrons, so the number of valence electrons is the group number

- Valence shell fills from the left (1 electron) to the right (8 electrons)

- Collectively, the essential elements for life on Earth, comprising 80% of the Earth's surface

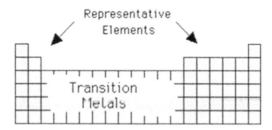

Representative elements have s and p orbitals, while transitions metals have d orbitals

Alkali metals

The alkali metals (Group 1 or formerly 1A) include the elements Li, Na, K, Rb, Cs, and Fr, and the properties of the alkali metals are as follows:

- Single valence electron that is easily ionized. Therefore, they have low ionization energy and are very reactive

- React to lose one electron and form a cation with +1 oxidation state

- More reactive from top to bottom because of increasing atomic radii (Cs and Fr most reactive)

- Malleable, ductile, good conductor like all metals, but usually softer than other metals

- React with oxygen to form strongly alkaline oxides

- React with water to form hydroxides and hydrogen

- React with acids to form salts and releases hydrogen

- Commonly found in nature as compounds with halogens

Alkaline earth metals

The alkaline earth metals (Group 2 or formerly 2A) include Be, Mg, Ca, Sr, Ba, and Ra, and the properties of the alkaline earth metals are:

- 2 valence electrons, so relatively low ionization energy and reactive

- React to lose two electrons and form cation with +2 oxidation state

- Increasingly reactive from top to bottom because of the increasing atomic radii

- React with oxygen to form strongly alkaline oxides

- React with water to form hydroxides and hydrogen

- React with acids to form salts and releases hydrogen

- Due to their reactivity, generally not found in nature

Oxygen group

The oxygen group, also known as the chalcogens (Group 16 or formerly VIA), includes O, S, Se, Te, Po, and Lv, and the properties of the chalcogens are as follows:

- Oxygen, sulfur, and selenium are nonmetals, while tellurium and polonium are metalloids

- Lighter chalcogens (O, S) are typically non-toxic and critical to life, while heavier chalcogens are toxic

- Form ions with multiple oxidation numbers; sulfur's oxidation states are between -2 to $+6$

- Exist as polyatomic molecules in the elemental state (e.g., O_2, S_8)

Halogens

The halogens (Group 17 or formerly as 7A) include F, Cl, Br, I and At, and the properties of halogens are as follows:

- 7 valence electrons (2 from *s* subshell and 5 from *p* subshell) - high electron affinity, very reactive (most reactive of all nonmetals)

- Most electronegative of all the elements

- React to gain one electron and achieve full valence shell; forms anions with –1 oxidation state

- Less reactive from top to bottom because of decreasing atomic radii

- React with alkali metals and alkaline earth metals to form salts (crystalline ionic solids)

- Form diatomic molecules in the elemental state (e.g., Cl_2, Br_2, I_2)

Noble gases - physical and chemical characteristics

The noble gases (Group 18 or formerly as 8A) include He, Ne, Ar, Kr, Xe, Rn and Og, and the properties of the noble gases are as follows:

- Full valence shell of 8 have high ionization energy coupled with a low electron affinity

- Inert (i.e., very unreactive); only heavier elements of the group react with few very electronegative elements, such as fluorine

- Exist in nature as monatomic gases (e.g., He, Ne, Ar)

Transition metals

The transition metals (Groups 3-11 or formerly as 3B-1B) have unique chemical properties due to their loosely bound outermost *d* orbital electrons, and the properties of the transition metals are as follows:

- High conductivity and malleability due to loosely bound, free-flowing outer *d* electrons.

- When bonded with other ions to form metal complexes, the *d* orbitals become non-degenerate (different energy).

  Electron transitions between non-degenerate *d* orbitals give transition metal complexes vivid colors.

- Lose electrons from more than one shell to form cations of different oxidation states, indicated using Roman numerals (e.g., Iron (II) Fe^{2+} and Iron (III) Fe^{3+})

The periodic table is represented with two detached rows of elements located under the table (the *f*-block). Those elements are collectively known as *inner transition elements* or the *lanthanide and actinide series*. They are in the 6th and 7th periods starting at the 5*d* block of the periodic table.

The inner transition elements were once classified as rare-earth elements due to the scarcity with which they naturally form.

However, even the rarest of all the inner transition metals was still more common than the platinum-group metals (which are transition metals).

Most inner-transition metals, including plutonium and uranium, only exist in nature in radioactive form and decay rapidly.

Metals

According to their shared physical and chemical properties, the elements are divided into metals, nonmetals, and metalloids.

Highly ordered, closely-packed atoms characterize metals.

The metals comprise almost three-fourths of all known Earth elements, such as aluminum, iron, calcium, and magnesium.

Many of the chemical and physical properties of metals result from their metallic bonds, where the valence electrons of *s* and *p* orbitals delocalize and form an aggregate of electrons that surround the nuclei of the interacting metal atoms.

The high degree of freedom with which their outermost electrons move between metal atoms gives rise to many of the following properties:

- Metallic luster - can shine or reflect light

- Malleable - can be hammered or rolled into thin sheets

- Ductile - can be drawn into wire

- Hardness ranges from hard (iron, chromium) to soft (sodium, lead, copper)

- Conduct heat and electricity

- Crystalline solids at room temperature, except mercury (Hg), which is the only liquid metal

- High melting point

- Chemical reactivity varies. Some are very unreactive (e.g., Au, Pt) while others are very reactive and will burst into flames upon contact with water (e.g., Na, K)

Nonmetals

The nonmetals are substances that do not exhibit any chemical or physical traits most associated with metal elements because they bond with each other to form covalently bonded compounds.

The nonmetals are in the upper right-hand corner of the periodic table and exhibit the following properties:

- Mostly polyatomic elements, except the monoatomic noble gases

- At room temperature, nonmetal elements can be found in all phases: gas (H_2, O_2, N_2, F_2, Cl_2), solid (I_2, Se_8, S_8, P_4), and liquid (Br_2)

- Brittle – they pulverize when struck

- Insulators (or extremely poor conductors) of electricity and heat, because electrons do not possess the high degree of movement as those in metal atoms

- Chemical reactivity ranges from inert (noble gases) to reactive (F_2, O_2, H_2). Nonmetals react with metals to form ionic compounds

- Some nonmetals have allotropes: different forms in the same phase (carbon as diamond and graphite)

Differences between metals and nonmetals

Chemical Properties	
Metals	**Nonmetals**
Likes to lose electrons to gain a positive (+) oxidation state (good reducing agent)	Likes to gain electrons to form a negative (−) oxidation state (good oxidizing agent)
Lower electronegativity – partially positive in a covalent bond with nonmetal	Higher electronegativity – partially negative in a covalent bond with metal
Forms basic oxides	Forms acidic oxides
Physical Properties	
Good conductor of heat and electricity	Poor conductor of heat and electricity
Malleable, ductile, luster, and solid at room temperature (except Hg)	Solid, liquid, or gas at room temperature. Brittle if solid and without luster.

Metalloids (e.g., B, Si, As) exhibit properties of both metals and nonmetals. The metalloids are in a "stair-step" line of the periodic table that divides metals and nonmetals. Some metalloids are lustrous like metals, while others are brittle like nonmetals. Metalloids are also unique because they do not typically conduct electricity at room temperatures but conduct electricity when heated to higher temperatures.

Notes

Notes

Notes

Electronic Structure and the Periodic Table

Practice Questions
and
Detailed Explanations

Practice Questions

==

Practice Set 1: Questions 1–20

==

1. The property defined as the energy required to remove one electron from an atom in the gaseous state is:

    A. electronegativity

    B. ionization energy

    C. electron affinity

    D. hyperconjugation

    E. none of the above

2. Which of the following elements most easily accepts an extra electron?

    A. He

    B. Ca

    C. Cl

    D. Fr

    E. Na

3. Which of the following pairs has one metalloid element and one nonmetal element?

    A. ^{82}Pb and ^{83}Bi

    B. ^{19}K and ^{9}F

    C. ^{51}Sb and ^{20}Ca

    D. ^{33}As and ^{14}Si

    E. ^{32}Ge and ^{9}F

4. Periods on the periodic table represent elements:

A. in the same group

B. with consecutive atomic numbers

C. known as isotopes

D. with similar chemical properties

E. known as ions

5. How many electrons can occupy the $n = 2$ shell?

A. 2

B. 6

C. 8

D. 18

E. 32

6. Ignoring hydrogen and helium, which area(s) of the periodic table contain(s) both metals and nonmetals?

      I. *s* area   II. *p* area   III. *d* area

A. I only

B. II only

C. III only

D. I and II only

E. I, II and III

7. What is the number of known nonmetals relative to the number of metals?

A. About two times greater

B. About fifty percent

C. About five times less

D. About twenty-five percent greater

E. About three times greater

8. Based on experimental evidence, Dalton postulated that:

    A. atoms of different elements have the same mass

    B. not all atoms of a given element are identical

    C. atoms can be created and destroyed in chemical reactions

    D. each element consists of indivisible minute particles called atoms

    E. none of the above

9. Which statement is true regarding the average mass of a naturally occurring isotope of iron that has an atomic mass equal to 55.91 amu?

    A. 55.91 / 1.0078 times greater than a ^{1}H atom

    B. 55.91 / 12.000 times greater than a ^{12}C atom

    C. 55.91 times greater than a ^{12}C atom

    D. 55.91 times greater than a ^{1}H atom

    E. none of the above

10. Which is the principal quantum number?

    A. n

    B. m

    C. l

    D. s

    E. $+\frac{1}{2}$

11. How many electrons can occupy the $4s$ subshell?

    A. 1

    B. 2

    C. 6

    D. 8

    E. 10

12. An excited hydrogen atom emits a light spectrum of specific, characteristic wavelengths. The light spectrum is a result of:

    A. energy released as H atoms form H_2 molecules

    B. the light wavelengths, which are not absorbed by valence electrons when white light passes through the sample

    C. particles being emitted as the hydrogen nuclei decay

    D. excited electrons being promoted to higher energy levels

    E. excited electrons dropping to lower energy levels

13. Which has the largest radius?

    A. Br^-

    B. K^+

    C. Ar

    D. Ca^{2+}

    E. Cl^-

14. In its ground state, how many unpaired electrons does a sulfur atom have?

    A. 0

    B. 1

    C. 2

    D. 3

    E. 4

15. Which of the elements would be in the same group as the element whose electronic configuration is $1s^2 2s^2 2p^6 3s^2 3p^6 4s^1$?

    A. Ar

    B. Se

    C. Mg

    D. P

    E. Li

16. When an atom is most stable, how many electrons does it contain in its valence shell?

   A. 4
   B. 6
   C. 8
   D. 10
   E. 12

17. Which characteristic(s) is/are responsible for the changes seen in the first ionization energy when moving down a column?

     I. Increased shielding of electrons

     II. Larger atomic radii

     III. Increasing nuclear attraction for electrons

   A. I only
   B. II only
   C. III only
   D. I and II only
   E. I, II and III

18. What is the maximum number of electrons that can occupy the $4f$ subshell?

   A. 6
   B. 8
   C. 14
   D. 16
   E. 18

19. The property that describes the energy released by a gas phase atom from adding an electron is:

   A. ionization energy
   B. electronegativity
   C. electron affinity
   D. hyperconjugation
   E. none of the above

20. The attraction of the nucleus on the outermost electron in an atom tends to:

A. decrease from right to left and bottom to top on the periodic table

B. decrease from left to right and bottom to top on the periodic table

C. decrease from left to right and top to bottom of the periodic table

D. increase from right to left and top to bottom on the periodic table

E. decrease from right to left and top to bottom on the periodic table

===

Practice Set 2: Questions 21–40

===

21. How many protons and neutrons are in ^{35}Cl, respectively?

  A. 35; 18
  B. 18; 17
  C. 17; 18
  D. 17; 17
  E. 35; 17

22. What must be the same if two atoms represent the same element?

  A. number of neutrons
  B. atomic mass
  C. number of electron shells
  D. atomic number
  E. number of valence electrons

23. Referring to the periodic table, which of the following is NOT a solid metal under normal conditions?

  A. Ce
  B. Os
  C. Ba
  D. Cr
  E. Hg

24. Which of the following describe electron affinity?

      I. Ability of an atom to attract electrons when it bonds with another atom

      II. Energy needed to remove an electron from a neutral atom of the element in the gas phase

      III. Energy liberated when an electron is added to a gaseous neutral atom converting it to an anion

  A. I only

  B. II only

  C. III only

  D. I and II only

  E. I, II and III

25. Metalloids are elements:

  A. larger than nonmetals

  B. found in asteroids

  C. smaller than metals

  D. that have some properties like metals and some like nonmetals

  E. that have properties different from either the metals or the nonmetals

26. Which of the following represent(s) halogens?

      I. Br   II. H   III. I

  A. I only

  B. II only

  C. III only

  D. I and III

  E. I and II

27. According to John Dalton, atoms of an element:

  A. are divisible

  B. have the same shape

  C. are identical

  D. have different masses

  E. none of the above

28. Which of the following represents a pair of isotopes?

    A. $^{32}_{16}S$, $^{32}_{16}S^{2-}$

    B. O_2, O_3

    C. $^{14}_{6}C$, $^{14}_{7}N$

    D. $^{1}_{1}H$, $^{2}_{1}H$

    E. None of the above

29. Early investigators proposed that the ray of the cathode tube was a negatively charged particle because the ray was:

    A. not seen from the positively charged anode

    B. diverted by a magnetic field

    C. observed in the presence or absence of a gas

    D. able to change colors depending on which gas was within the tube

    E. attracted to positively charged electric plates

30. What is the value of quantum numbers n and l in the highest occupied orbital for the element carbon with an atomic number of 6?

    A. $n = 1, l = 1$

    B. $n = 2, l = 1$

    C. $n = 1, l = 2$

    D. $n = 2, l = 2$

    E. $n = 3, l = 3$

31. Which type of subshell is filled by the distinguishing electron in an alkaline earth metal?

    A. s

    B. p

    C. f

    D. d

    E. both s and p

32. If an element has an electron configuration ending in $3p^4$, which statements about the element's electron configuration is NOT correct?

   A. There are six electrons in the 3rd shell

   B. Five different subshells contain electrons

   C. There are eight electrons in the 2nd shell

   D. The 3rd shell needs two more electrons to be filled

   E. All are correct statements

33. Halogens form anions by:

A. gaining two electrons

B. gaining one electron

C. gaining one neutron

D. losing one electron

E. losing two electrons

34. What is the term for a broad, uninterrupted band of radiant energy?

   A. Ultraviolet spectrum

   B. Visible spectrum

   C. Continuous spectrum

   D. Radiant energy spectrum

   E. None of the above

35. Which of the following is the correct order of increasing atomic radius?

   A. Te < Sb < In < Sr < Rb

   B. In < Sb < Te < Sr < Rb

   C. Te < Sb < In < Rb < Sr

   D. Rb < Sr < In < Sb < Te

   E. In < Sb < Te < Rb < Sr

36. Which of the following electron configurations represents an excited state of an atom?

   A. $1s^2 2s^2 2p^6 3s^2 3p^3$

   B. $1s^2 2s^2 2p^6 3s^2 3p^6 4s^1$

   C. $1s^2 2s^2 2p^6 3d^1$

   D. $1s^2 2s^2 2p^6 3s^2 3p^6 4s^2 3d^1$

   E. $1s^2 2s^2 2p^6 3s^2 3p^6 4s^2 3d^{10} 4p^1$

37. Which of the following elements has the greatest ionization energy?

   A. rubidium

   B. neon

   C. potassium

   D. calcium

   E. magnesium

38. Which of the following elements is a nonmetal?

   A. Sodium

   B. Chlorine

   C. Aluminum

   D. Magnesium

   E. Palladium

39. An atom that contains 47 protons, 47 electrons, and 60 neutrons is an isotope of:

   A. Nd

   B. Bh

   C. Ag

   D. Al

   E. cannot be determined

40. The shell level of an electron is defined by which quantum number?

    A. electron spin quantum number

    B. magnetic quantum number

    C. azimuthal quantum number

    D. principal quantum number

    E. principal quantum number and electron spin quantum number

==

Practice Set 3: Questions 41–60

==

41. How many neutrons are in a Beryllium atom with an atomic number of 4 and atomic mass of 9?

  A. 4
  B. 5
  C. 9
  D. 13
  E. 18

42. Which characteristics describe the mass, charge, and location of an electron, respectively?

  A. approximate mass 5×10^{-4} amu; charge -1; outside nucleus
  B. approximate mass 5×10^{-4} amu; charge 0; inside nucleus
  C. approximate mass 1 amu; charge -1; inside nucleus
  D. approximate mass 1 amu; charge $+1$; outside nucleus
  E. approximate mass 1 amu; charge 0; outside nucleus

43. What is the name of the compound $CaCl_2$?

  A. dichloromethane
  B. dichlorocalcium
  C. carbon chloride
  D. calcium chloride
  E. dicalcium chloride

44. What is the name for elements in the same column of the periodic table with similar chemical properties?

  A. congeners
  B. stereoisomers
  C. diastereomers
  D. epimers
  E. anomers

45. Which of the following sets of elements consist of members of the same group on the periodic table?

    A. ^{14}Si, ^{15}P and ^{16}S

    B. ^{20}Ca, ^{26}Fe and ^{34}Se

    C. ^{9}F, ^{10}Ne and ^{11}Na

    D. ^{31}Ga, ^{49}In and ^{81}Tl

    E. ^{11}Na, ^{20}Ca and ^{39}Y

46. Which element would most likely be a metal with a low melting point?

    A. K

    B. B

    C. N

    D. C

    E. Cl

47. Mg is an example of a(n):

    A. transition metal

    B. noble gas

    C. alkali metal

    D. halogen

    E. alkaline earth metal

48. Metalloids:

    I. have some metallic and some nonmetallic properties

    II. may have low electrical conductivities

    III. contain elements in Group IIIB

    A. I and III only

    B. II only

    C. II and III only

    D. I and II only

    E. I, II and III

49. Which element is a halogen?

   A. Os

   B. I

   C. O

   D. Te

   E. Se

50. Silicon exists as three isotopes: ^{28}Si, ^{29}Si, and ^{30}Si with atomic masses of 27.98 amu, 28.98 amu, and 29.97 amu, respectively. Which isotope is the most abundant in nature?

   A. ^{28}Si

   B. ^{29}Si

   C. ^{30}Si

   D. ^{28}Si and ^{30}Si are equally abundant

   E. All are equally abundant

51. Which statement supports why early investigators proposed that the ray of the cathode ray tube was due to the cathode?

   A. The ray was diverted by a magnetic field

   B. The ray was not seen from the positively charged anode

   C. The ray was attracted to the electric plates that were positively charged

   D. The ray changed color depending on the gas used within the tube

   E. The ray was observed in the presence or absence of a gas

52. Which of the following is implied by the spin quantum number?

      I. The two spinning electrons generate magnetic fields

      II. The values are $+\frac{1}{2}$ or $-\frac{1}{2}$

      III. Orbital electrons have opposite spins

   A. II only

   B. I and II only

   C. I and III only

   D. II and III only

   E. I, II and III

53. How many quantum numbers are needed to describe a single electron in an atom?

   A. 1

   B. 2

   C. 3

   D. 4

   E. 5

54. Which of the following has the correct order of increasing energy in a subshell?

   A. 3s, 3p, 4s, 3d, 4p, 5s, 4d

   B. 3s, 3p, 4s, 3d, 4p, 4d, 5s

   C. 3s, 3p, 3d, 4s, 4p, 4d, 5s

   D. 3s, 3p, 3d, 4s, 4p, 5s, 4d

   E. 3s, 3p, 4s, 3d, 4d, 4p, 5s

55. Rank the elements below in the order of decreasing atomic radius.

   A. Al > P > Cl > Na > Mg

   B. Cl > Al > P > Na > Mg

   C. Mg > Na > P > Al > Cl

   D. Na > Mg > Al > P > Cl

   E. P > Al > Cl > Mg > Na

56. Which of the following is the electron configuration of a boron atom?

   A. $1s^2 2s^1 2p^2$

   B. $1s^2 2p^3$

   C. $1s^2 2s^2 2p^2$

   D. $1s^2 2s^2 2p^1$

   E. $1s^2 2s^1 2p^1$

57. Which element has the electron configuration
$1s^2 2s^2 2p^6 3s^2 3p^6 4s^2 3d^{10} 4p^6 5s^2 4d^{10} 5p^2$?

   A. Sn

   B. As

   C. Pb

   D. Sb

   E. In

58. Which of the following elements has the greatest ionization energy?

   A. Ar

   B. Sr

   C. Br

   D. In

   E. Sn

59. Which element has the lowest electronegativity?

   A. Mg

   B. Al

   C. Cl

   D. Br

   E. I

60. Refer to the periodic table and predict which of the following is a solid nonmetal under normal conditions.

   A. Cl

   B. F

   C. Se

   D. As

   E. Ar

Notes

===

Practice Set 4: Questions 61–80

===

61. Lines were observed in the spectrum of uranium ore (i.e., naturally occurring solid material) identical to those of helium in the spectrum of the Sun. Which of the following produced the lines in the helium spectrum?

   A. Excited protons jumping to a higher energy level

   B. Excited protons dropping to a lower energy level

   C. Excited electrons jumping to a higher energy level

   D. Excited electrons dropping to a lower energy level

   E. None of the above

62. Which set of quantum numbers is possible?

   A. $n = 1; l = 2; m_l = 3; m_s = -\frac{1}{2}$

   B. $n = 4; l = 2; m_l = 2; m_s = -\frac{1}{2}$

   C. $n = 2; l = 1; m_l = 2; m_s = -\frac{1}{2}$

   D. $n = 3; l = 3; m_l = 2; m_s = -\frac{1}{2}$

   E. $n = 2; l = 3; m_l = 2; m_s = -\frac{1}{2}$

63. The number of neutrons in an atom is equal to:

   A. the mass number

   B. the atomic number

   C. mass number minus the atomic number

   D. atomic number minus the mass number

   E. mass number plus the atomic number

64. Which of the following represent(s) a compound rather than an element?

   I. O_3 II. CCl_4 III. S_8

   A. I and III only

   B. II only

   C. I and II only

   D. III only

   E. I only

---

65. Which of the following elements is NOT correctly classified?

   A. Mo – transition element
   B. Sr – alkaline earth metal
   C. K – representative element
   D. Ar – noble gas
   E. Po – halogen

66. Which is the name of the elements that have properties of both metals and nonmetals?

   A. alkaline earth metals
   B. metalloids
   C. nonmetals
   D. metals
   E. halogens

67. Which of the following is the correct sequence of atomic radii from smallest to largest?

   A. $Al < S < Al^{3+} < S^{2-}$
   B. $S < S^{2-} < Al < Al^{3+}$
   C. $Al^{3+} < Al < S^{2-} < S$
   D. $Al^{3+} < S < S^{2-} < Al$
   E. $Al < Al^{3+} < S^{2-} < S$

68. Which of the following elements contains 6 valence electrons?

   A. S
   B. Cl
   C. Si
   D. P
   E. Ca^{2+}

69. From the periodic table, which of the following elements is a semimetal?

A. Ar

B. As

C. Al

D. Ac

E. Am

70. Which statement does NOT describe the noble gases?

A. The more massive noble gases react with other elements

B. They belong to Group VIIIA (or 18)

C. They contain at least one metalloid

D. He, Ne, Ar, Kr, Xe and Rn are included in the group

E. They were once known as the inert gases

71. Which is a good experimental method to distinguish between ordinary hydrogen and deuterium, the rare isotope of hydrogen?

> I. Measure the density of the gas at STP
> II. Measure the rate at which the gas effuses
> III. Infrared spectroscopy

A. I only

B. II only

C. I and II only

D. I, II and III

E. II and III only

72. Which statement is true regarding the relative abundances of the ^{6}lithium or ^{7}lithium isotopes?

A. The relative proportions change as neutrons move between the nuclei

B. The isotopes are in roughly equal proportions

C. The relative ratio depends on the temperature of the element

D. ^{6}Lithium is much more abundant

E. ^{7}Lithium is much more abundant

73. Which represents the charge on 1 mole of electrons?

  A. 96,485 C

  B. 6.02×10^{23} C

  C. 6.02×10^{23} grams

  D. 1 C

  E. 1 e

74. Which of the following statement(s) is/are true?

   I. The *f* subshell contains 7 orbitals

   II. The *d* subshell contains 5 orbitals

   III. The third energy shell ($n = 3$) has no *f* orbitals

  A. I only

  B. II only

  C. I and II only

  D. II and III only

  E. I, II and III

75. Which element has the greatest ionization energy?

  A. Fr

  B. Cl

  C. Ga

  D. I

  E. Cs

76. Electrons fill subshells in order of:

   I. decreasing distance from the nucleus

   II. increasing distance from the nucleus

   III. increasing energy

  A. I only

  B. II only

  C. I and II only

  D. II and III only

  E. I, II and III

---

77. Which of the following produces the "atomic fingerprint" of an element?

    A. Excited protons dropping to a lower energy level

    B. Excited protons jumping to a higher energy level

    C. Excited electrons dropping to a lower energy level

    D. Excited electrons jumping to a higher energy level

    E. None of the above

78. Which of the following is the electron configuration for manganese (Mn)?

    A. $1s^2 2s^2 2p^6 3s^2 3p^6$

    B. $1s^2 2s^2 2p^6 3s^2 3p^6 4s^2 3d^{10} 4p^1$

    C. $1s^2 2s^2 2p^6 3s^2 3p^6 4s^2 3d^6$

    D. $1s^2 2s^2 2p^6 3s^2 3p^6 4s^2 3d^8$

    E. $1s^2 2s^2 2p^6 3s^2 3p^6 4s^2 3d^5$

79. Which element listed below has the greatest electronegativity?

    A. I

    B. Fr

    C. H

    D. He

    E. F

80. Which of the following is NOT an alkali metal?

    A. Fr

    B. Cs

    C. Ca

    D. Na

    E. Rb

Notes

Practice Set 5: Questions 81–104

81. What is the atomic number and the mass number of ^{79}Br, respectively?

    A. 35; 44

    B. 44; 35

    C. 35; 79

    D. 79; 35

    E. 35; 114

82. Both ^{65}Cu and ^{65}Zn have the same:

    A. mass number

    B. number of neutrons

    C. number of ions

    D. number of electrons

    E. number of protons

83. Which of the following statements best describes an element?

    A. has consistent physical properties

    B. consists of more than one type of atom

    C. consists of only one type of atom

    D. material that is pure

    E. material that has consistent chemical properties

84. Which element(s) is/are alkali metal(s)?

    I. Na   II. Sr   III. Cs

    A. I and II only

    B. I and III only

    C. I only

    D. II only

    E. I, II and III

85. Which of the following is/are a general characteristic of a nonmetallic element?

      I. reacts with metals   II. pliable   III. shiny luster

A. I only

B. II only

C. III only

D. I and II only

E. I, II and III

86. Which Group of the periodic table has 3 nonmetals?

A. Group IIIA

B. Group IVA

C. Group VA

D. Group IA

E. Group VIA

87. The transition metals occur in which period(s) on the periodic table?

      I. 2   II. 3   III. 4

A. I only

B. II only

C. III only

D. I and III only

E. I, II and III

88. Which of Dalton's original proposals is/are still valid?

      I. Compounds contain atoms in small whole-number ratios

      II. Atoms of different elements combine to form compounds

      III. An element is composed of tiny particles called atoms

A. I only

B. II only

C. III only

D. I and III only

E. I, II and III

89. Given that parent and daughter nuclei are isotopes of the same element, the ratio of α to β decay produced by the parent must be:

A. 1 to 1

B. 1 to 2

C. 2 to 1

D. 2 to 3

E. 3 to 2

90. ^{63}Cu isotope makes up 69% of the naturally occurring Cu. If only one other isotope is present for natural copper, what is it?

A. ^{59}Cu

B. ^{65}Cu

C. ^{61}Cu

D. ^{62}Cu

E. ^{60}Cu

91. Which does NOT contain cathode ray particles?

A. H_2O

B. K

C. H

D. He

E. All contain cathode ray particles

92. Which principle or rule states that only two electrons can occupy an orbital?

A. Pauli exclusion principle

B. Hund's rule

C. Heisenberg uncertainty principle

D. Newton's principle

E. None of the above

93. What is the maximum number of electrons to fill the atom's second electron shell?

A. 18

B. 2

C. 4

D. 12

E. 8

94. How many electrons can occupy the $4d$ subshell?

A. 2

B. 6

C. 8

D. 10

E. 12

95. The f subshell contains:

A. 1 orbital

B. 3 orbitals

C. 5 orbitals

D. 7 orbitals

E. 9 orbitals

96. When an excited electron returns to the ground state, it releases:

A. photons

B. protons

C. beta particles

D. alpha particles

E. gamma rays

97. Which statement is true of the energy levels for an electron in a hydrogen atom?

  A. The energy levels are identical to the levels in the He^+ ion

  B. The energy of each level can be computed from a known formula

  C. The distance between energy levels for $n = 1$ and $n = 2$ is the same as the distance between the $n = 3$ and $n = 4$ energy levels

  D. Since there is only one electron, the electron must be located in the lowest energy level

  E. The distance between the $n = 3$ and $n = 4$ energy levels in the same as the distance between the $n = 4$ and $n = 5$ energy levels

98. An ion is represented by which of the following electron configurations?

    I. $1s^22s^22p^6$ II. $1s^22s^22p^63s^2$ III. $1s^22s^22p^23s^23p^6$

  A. I only

  B. II only

  C. I and II only

  D. II and III only

  E. I, II and III

99. Consider an atom with the electron configuration $1s^22s^22p^63s^23p^6$. Which of the following is an accurate statement concerning this atom?

  A. This atom would probably be chemically inert

  B. This atom has a non-zero angular momentum

  C. This atom is in an excited state

  D. The atomic number of this atom is $Z = 11$

  E. This atom is most likely to give rise to an ion with a charge of +2

100. A halogen is expected to have [ ] ionization energy and [ ] electron affinity?

  A. low; small

  B. low; large

  C. high; large

  D. high; small

  E. high; neutral

101. Why does a chlorine atom form an anion more easily than a cation?

   A. Chlorine has a high electronegativity value

   B. Chlorine has a large positive electron affinity

   C. Chlorine donates one electron to complete its outer shell

   D. Chlorine gains one electron to complete its outer shell

   E. Chlorine has a low electronegativity value

102. What is the approximate mass number of an element if one mole weighs 12 grams?

   A. 6.02×10^{23}

   B. 12

   C. 1

   D. $12 \times 6.02 \times 10^{23}$

   E. 24

103. How many neutrons are in the most common isotope of hydrogen?

   A. 0

   B. 1

   C. 2

   D. 3

   E. 4

104. Which of the following molecules does NOT exist?

   A. OF_5

   B. $KLiCO_3$

   C. ICl

   D. UF_6

   E. All of the above exist

Notes

Notes

Detailed Explanations

===

Practice Set 1: Questions 1–20

===

1. B is correct.

Ionization energy (IE) is the amount of energy required to remove the most loosely bound electron of an isolated gaseous atom to form a cation. This is an endothermic process.

Ionization energy is expressed as:

$$X + energy \rightarrow X^+ + e^-$$

where X is an atom (or molecule) capable of being ionized (i.e., having an electron removed), X^+ is that atom or molecule after an electron is removed, and e^- is the removed electron.

The principal quantum number (n) describes the size of the orbital and the energy of an electron, and the most probable distance from the nucleus. It refers to the size of the orbital and the energy level of an electron.

The elements with larger shell sizes (n is large) listed at the bottom of the periodic table have low ionization energies. This is due to the shielding (by the inner shell electrons) from the nucleus's positive charge. The greater the distance between the electrons and the nucleus, the less energy is needed to remove the outer valence electrons.

2. C is correct.

Accepting electrons to form anions is a characteristic of non-metals to obtain the noble gases' electron configuration (i.e., complete octet).

Except for helium (which has a complete octet with 2 electrons, $1s^2$), the noble gases have complete octets with ns^2 and np^6 orbitals.

Donating electrons to form cations (e.g., Ca^{2+}, Fr^+, Na^+) is a characteristic of metals to obtain the noble gases' electron configuration (i.e., complete octet).

3. E is correct.

Metalloids are semimetallic elements (i.e., between metals and nonmetals). The metalloids are boron (B), silicon (Si), germanium (Ge), arsenic (As), antimony (Sb) and tellurium (Te). Some literature reports polonium (Po) and astatine (At) as metalloids.

Seventeen elements are generally classified as nonmetals. Eleven are gases: hydrogen (H), helium (He), nitrogen (N), oxygen (O), fluorine (F), neon (Ne), chlorine (Cl), argon (Ar), krypton (Kr), xenon (Xe) and radon (Rn). One nonmetal is a liquid – bromine (Br) – and five are solids: carbon (C), phosphorus (P), sulfur (S), selenium (Se) and iodine (I).

4. B is correct.

An element is a pure chemical substance that consists of a single type of atom, distinguished by its atomic number (Z) (i.e., the number of protons it contains). 118 elements have been identified, of which the first 94 occur naturally on Earth, with the remaining 24 being synthetic elements.

The properties of the elements on the periodic table repeat at regular intervals, creating "groups" or "families" of elements. Each column on the periodic table is a group, and elements within each group have similar physical and chemical characteristics due to the orbital location of their outermost electron. These groups only exist because the elements of the periodic table are listed by increasing atomic number.

5. C is correct.

For $n = 2$ shell, it has 2 orbitals: s, p

Each orbital can hold two electrons.

A maximum number of electrons in each shell:

The s subshell has 1 spherical orbital and can accommodate 2 electrons.

The p subshell has 3 dumbbell-shaped orbitals accommodating 6 electrons.

Maximum number of electrons in $n = 2$ shell is:

2 (for s) + 6 (for p) = 8 electrons

6. B is correct.

Groups IVA, VA and VIA each contain at least one metal and one nonmetal.

Group IVA has three metals (tin, lead, and flerovium) and one nonmetal (carbon).

Group VA has two metals (bismuth and moscovium) and two nonmetals (nitrogen and phosphorous).

Group VIA has one metal (livermorium) and three nonmetals (oxygen, sulfur, and selenium).

All three groups are part of the *p*-block of the periodic table.

14 IVA 4A	15 VA 5A	16 VIA 6A
6 $^{+4,+3,+2,+1}_{-4,-3}$ $^{-2,-1}$ **C** Carbon 12.011	7 $^{+5,+3,-3}$ **N** Nitrogen 14.007	8 $^{-2}$ **O** Oxygen 15.999
14 $^{+4,-4}$ **Si** Silicon 28.086	15 $^{+5,+3,-3}$ **P** Phosphorus 30.974	16 $^{+6,+4,+2,-2}$ **S** Sulfur 32.066
32 $^{+4,+2,-4}$ **Ge** Germanium 72.631	33 $^{+5,+3,-3}$ **As** Arsenic 74.922	34 $^{+6,+4,+2,-2}$ **Se** Selenium 78.971
50 $^{+4,+2,-4}$ **Sn** Tin 118.711	51 $^{+5,+3,-3}$ **Sb** Antimony 121.760	52 $^{+6,+4,+2,-2}$ **Te** Tellurium 127.6
82 $^{+4,+2}$ **Pb** Lead 207.2	83 $^{+3}$ **Bi** Bismuth 208.980	84 $^{+4,+2,-2}$ **Po** Polonium [208.982]
114 unknown **Fl** Flerovium [289]	115 unknown **Mc** Moscovium [289]	116 unknown **Lv** Livermorium [293]

7. C is correct.

The majority of elements on the periodic table (over 100 elements) are metals. Currently, there are 84 metal elements on the Periodic Table.

Seventeen elements are generally classified as nonmetals. Eleven are gases: hydrogen (H), helium (He), nitrogen (N), oxygen (O), fluorine (F), neon (Ne), chlorine (Cl), argon (Ar), krypton (Kr), xenon (Xe) and radon (Rn). One nonmetal is a liquid – bromine (Br) – and five are solids: carbon (C), phosphorus (P), sulfur (S), selenium (Se) and iodine (I).

Therefore, with the ratio of 84:17, there are about five times more metals than nonmetals.

8. D is correct.

English chemist John Dalton is known for his Atomic Theory, which states that *elements are made of small particles called atoms, which cannot be created or destroyed.*

9. B is correct.

Isotopes are variants of a particular element, which differ in the number of neutrons. All isotopes of the element have the same number of protons and occupy the same position on the periodic table.

The number of protons within the atom's nucleus is the atomic number (Z) and is equal to the number of electrons in the neutral (non-ionized) atom. Each atomic number identifies a specific element, but not the isotope; an atom of a given element may have a wide range in its number of neutrons.

The number of both protons and neutrons (i.e., nucleons) in the nucleus is the atom's mass number (A), and each isotope has a different mass number.

The atomic mass unit (amu) was designed using ^{12}C isotope as the reference.

1 amu = 1/12 mass of a ^{12}C atom.

Masses of other elements are measured against this standard.

If the mass of an atom 55.91 amu, the atom's mass is 55.91 × (1/12 mass of ^{12}C).

10. A is correct.

The three coordinates that come from Schrodinger's wave equations are the principal (n), angular (l) and magnetic (m) quantum numbers.

These quantum numbers describe the size, shape, and orientation of the orbitals.

The principal quantum number (n) describes the size of the orbital and the energy of an electron, and the most probable distance from the nucleus. It refers to the size of the orbital and the energy level of an electron.

The angular momentum quantum number (l) describes the shape of the orbital within the subshells.

The magnetic quantum number (m) determines the number of orbitals and their orientation within a subshell. Consequently, its value depends on the orbital angular momentum quantum number (l).

Given a certain l, m is an interval ranging from $-l$ to $+l$ (i.e., it can be zero, a negative integer, or a positive integer).

The s is the spin quantum number (e.g., $+\frac{1}{2}$ or $-\frac{1}{2}$).

11. B is correct.

Electron shells represent the orbit that electrons allow around an atom's nucleus. Each shell comprises one or more subshells, which are named using lowercase letters (s, p, d, f).

Subshell name	Subshell max electrons	Shell max electrons
1s	2	2
2s	2	$2 + 6 = 8$
2p	6	
3s	2	$2 + 6 + 10 = 18$
3p	6	
3d	10	
4s	2	$2 + 6 + 10 + 14 = 32$
4p	6	
4d	10	
4f	14	

The first shell has one subshell ($1s$); the second shell has two subshells ($2s, 2p$); the third shell has three subshells ($3s, 3p, 3d$).

An s subshell holds 2 electrons, and each subsequent subshell in the series can hold 4 more (p holds 6, d holds 10, f holds 14).

The shell number (i.e., principal quantum number) before the s (i.e., 4 in this example) does not affect how many electrons can occupy the subshell.

12. E is correct.

The specific, characteristic line spectra for atoms result from photons being emitted when excited electrons drop to lower energy levels.

13. A is correct.

In general, the size of neutral atoms increases down a group (i.e., increasing shell size) and decreases from left to right across the periodic table.

Negative ions (anions) are *much larger* than their neutral element.

Positive ions (cations) are *much smaller*.

All examples are isoelectronic because of the same number of electrons.

Atomic numbers:

Br = 35; K = 19; Ar = 18; Ca = 20 and Cl = 17

The atomic radius's general trend is to decrease from left to right and increase from top to bottom in the periodic table. When the ion gains or loses an electron to create a new charged ion, its radius would change slightly, but the general trend of radius still applies.

The ions K^+, Ca^{2+}, Cl^-, and Ar have identical numbers of electrons.

However, Br is located below Cl (larger principal quantum number, n), and its atomic number is almost twice the others. This indicates that Br has more electrons, and its radius must be significantly larger than the other atoms.

14. C is correct.

The ground state configuration of sulfur is $[Ne]3s^23p^4$.

According to Hund's rule, p orbitals are filled separately and then pair electrons by $+\frac{1}{2}$ or $-\frac{1}{2}$ spin.

The first three p electrons fill separate orbitals, and then the fourth electron pairs with two remaining unpaired electrons.

15. E is correct.

There are two common ways to obtain the proper answer to this problem:

1. Using an atomic number.

Calculate the atomic number by adding all the electrons:

$2 + 2 + 6 + 2 + 6 + 1 = 19$

Find element number 19 in the periodic table.

Check the group's location for other elements belonging to the same group.

Element number 19 is potassium (K), so the element that belongs to the same group (IA) is lithium (Li).

2. Using subshells.

Identify the outermost subshell and use it to identify its group in the periodic table:

In this problem, the outermost subshell is $4s^1$.

Relationship between outermost subshell and group:

s^1 = Group IA

s^2 = Group IIA

p^1 = Group IIIA

p^2 = Group IVA

...

p^6 = Group VIII A

d = transition element

f = lanthanide/actinide element

16. C is correct.

The number of valence electrons for an element can be determined by its group (i.e., vertical column) on the periodic table.

Except for the transition metals (i.e., groups 3-12), the group number identifies how many valence electrons are associated with a particular element: all elements of the same group have the same number of valence electrons.

Atoms are most stable when they contain 8 electrons (i.e., complete octet) in the valence shell.

17. D is correct.

The principal quantum number (n) describes the size of the orbital and the energy of an electron, and the most probable distance from the nucleus. It refers to the size of the orbital and the energy level of an electron.

The elements with larger shell sizes (n is large) listed at the bottom of the periodic table have low ionization energies. This is due to the shielding (by the inner shell electrons) from the nucleus's positive charge.

The greater the distance between the electrons and the nucleus, the less energy is needed to remove the outer valence electrons.

Ionization energy decreases with increasing shell size (i.e., n value) and generally increases to the right across a period (i.e., row) in the periodic table.

Moving down a column corresponds to increasing shell size with electrons further from the nucleus and decreasing nuclear attraction.

18. C is correct.

The *f* subshell has 7 orbitals.

Each orbital can hold two electrons.

The capacity of an *f* subshell is 7 orbitals × 2 electrons/orbital = 14 electrons.

19. C is correct.

The term "electron affinity" does not use the word energy as a reference; it is measurable energy, like ionization energy.

20. E is correct.

The nucleus's attraction on the outermost electrons determines the ionization energy, increasing the right and increases up on the periodic table.

===

Practice Set 2: Questions 21–40

===

21. C is correct.

The mass number (A) is the sum of protons and neutrons in an atom.

The mass number approximates the atomic weight of the element as amu (grams per mole).

The problem only specifies the atomic mass (A) of Cl: 35 amu.

The atomic number (Z) is not given, but the information is available in the periodic table (atomic number = 17).

> number of neutrons = atomic weight – atomic number
>
> number of neutrons = 35 – 17
>
> number of neutrons = 18

22. D is correct.

An element is a pure chemical substance that consists of a single type of atom, distinguished by its atomic number (Z) (i.e., the number of protons it contains).

118 elements have been identified, of which the first 94 occur naturally on Earth, with the remaining 24 being synthetic elements.

The properties of the elements on the periodic table repeat at regular intervals, creating "groups" or "families" of elements.

Each column on the periodic table is a group, and elements within each group have similar physical and chemical characteristics due to the orbital location of their outermost electron. These groups only exist because the elements of the periodic table are listed by increasing atomic number.

23. E is correct.

Metals are elements that form positive ions by losing electrons during chemical reactions. Thus metals are electropositive elements.

Metals are characterized by bright luster, hardness, resonate sound, and excellent heat and electricity conduction.

Metals, except mercury, are solids under normal conditions. Potassium has the lowest melting point of the solid metals at 146 °F.

24. C is correct.

Electron affinity is defined as the energy liberated when an electron is added to a gaseous neutral atom converting it to an anion.

25. D is correct.

Metalloids are semimetallic elements (i.e., between metals and nonmetals). The metalloids are boron (B), silicon (Si), germanium (Ge), arsenic (As), antimony (Sb) and tellurium (Te). Some literature reports polonium (Po) and astatine (At) as metalloids.

They have properties between metals and nonmetals. They typically have a metallic appearance but are only fair conductors of electricity (as opposed to metals that are excellent conductors), making them useable in the semiconductor industry.

Metalloids tend to be brittle, and chemically they behave more like nonmetals.

26. D is correct.

Halogens (Group VIIA) include fluorine (F), chlorine (Cl), bromine (Br), iodine (I) and astatine (At).

Halogens gain one electron to become a –1 anion, and the resulting ion has a complete octet of valence electrons.

27. C is correct.

Dalton's Atomic Theory, developed in the early 1800s, states that atoms of a given element are identical in mass and properties.

The masses of atoms of an element may not be identical, although all atoms of an element must have the same number of protons; they can have different numbers of neutrons (i.e., isotopes).

28. D is correct.

Elements are defined by the number of protons (i.e., atomic number).

The isotopes are neutral atoms: # electrons = # protons.

Isotopes are variants of a particular element that differ in the number of neutrons. All isotopes of the element have the same number of protons and occupy the same position on the periodic table.

> The subscript on the left denotes the number of protons.

> The superscript on the left denotes the number of protons and neutrons.

> The superscript on the right denotes the charge of an ion.

The number of protons within the atom's nucleus is the atomic number (Z) and is equal to the number of electrons in the neutral (non-ionized) atom. Each atomic number identifies a specific element, but not the isotope; an atom of a given element may have a wide range in its number of neutrons.

The number of both protons and neutrons (i.e., nucleons) in the nucleus is the atom's mass number (A), and each isotope of an element has a different mass number.

29. E is correct.

A cathode-ray particle is a different name for an electron.

Those particles (i.e., electrons) are attracted to the positively charged cathode, which implies that they are negatively charged.

30. B is correct.

The three coordinates that come from Schrodinger's wave equations are the principal (n), angular (l), and magnetic (m) quantum numbers.

These quantum numbers describe the size, shape, and orientation of the orbitals.

The principal quantum number (n) describes the size of the orbital, the energy of an electron, and the most probable distance from the nucleus. It refers to the size of the orbital and the energy level of an electron.

The angular momentum quantum number (l) describes the shape of the orbital of the subshells.

Carbon has an atomic number of 6 and an electron configuration of $1s^2$, $2s^2$, $2p^2$.

Therefore, electrons are in the second shell of $n = 2$, and two subshells are in the outermost shell of $l = 1$.

The values of l are 0 and 1, whereby only the largest value of l ($l = 1$) is reported.

31. A is correct.

The alkaline earth metals (Group IIA), in the ground state, have a filled s subshell with 2 electrons.

32. D is correct.

The 3rd shell consists of s, p and d subshells.

Each orbital can hold two electrons.

The s subshell has 1 spherical orbital and accommodates 2 electrons

The p subshell has 3 dumbbell-shaped orbitals and accommodates 6 e

The d subshell has 5 lobe-shaped orbitals and accommodates 10 e

1s
2s 2p
3s 3p 3d
4s 4p 4d 4f
5s 5p 5d 5f ...
6s 6p 6d ... ...

Order of filling orbitals

The $n = 3$ shell can accommodate a total of 18 electrons.

The element with the electron configuration terminating in $3p^4$ is sulfur (i.e., a total of 16 electrons).

33. B is correct.

Ions typically form with the same electron configuration as the noble gases. Except for helium (which has a complete octet with 2 electrons, $1s^2$), the noble gases have complete octets with ns^2 and np^6 orbitals.

Halogens (Group VIIA) include fluorine (F), chlorine (Cl), bromine (Br), iodine (I), and astatine (At).

Halogens gain one electron to become –1 anion, and the resulting ion has a complete octet of valence electrons.

34. C is correct.

A continuous spectrum refers to a broad, uninterrupted spectrum of radiant energy.

The visible spectrum refers to the light that humans can see and includes the colors of the rainbow.

The ultraviolet spectrum refers to electromagnetic radiation with a wavelength shorter than visible light but longer than X-rays.

The radiant energy spectrum refers to electromagnetic (EM) waves of all wavelengths.

However, the bands of frequency in an EM signal may be sharply defined with interruptions or broad.

35. A is correct.

In general, the size of neutral atoms increases down a group (i.e., increasing shell size) and decreases from left to right across the periodic table.

Positive ions (cations) are *much smaller* than the neutral element (due to greater effective nuclear charge).

Negative ions (anions) are *much larger* (due to smaller effective nuclear charge and repulsion of valence electrons).

36. C is correct.

In the ground state, the $3p$ orbitals fill before the $3d$ orbitals.

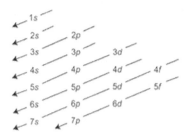

The lowest energy orbital fills before an orbital of a higher energy level.

Aufbau principle to determine the order of energy levels in subshells:

From the table above, the orbitals increase in energy from: $1s < 2s < 2p < 3s <$ $3p < 4s < 3d < 4p < 5s < 4d < 5p < 6s < 4f < 5d < 6p < 7s < 5f < 6d < 7p$

37. B is correct.

Ionization energy is defined as the energy needed to remove an electron from a neutral atom of the element in the gas phase.

The principal quantum number (n) describes the size of the orbital and the energy of an electron, and the most probable distance from the nucleus. It refers to the size of the orbital and the energy level of an electron.

The elements with larger shell sizes (n is large) listed at the bottom of the periodic table have low ionization energies. This is due to the shielding (by the inner shell electrons) from the nucleus's positive charge. The greater the distance between the electrons and the nucleus, the less energy is needed to remove the outer valence electrons.

Ionization energy decreases with increasing shell size (i.e., n value) and generally increases to the right across a period (i.e., row) in the periodic table.

Neon (Ne) has an atomic number of 10 and a shell size of $n = 2$.

Rubidium (Rb) has an atomic number of 37 and a shell size of $n = 5$.

Potassium (K) has an atomic number of 19 and a shell size of $n = 4$.

Calcium (Ca) has an atomic number of 20 and a shell size is $n = 4$.

Magnesium (Mg) has an atomic number of 12 and a shell size of $n = 3$.

38. B is correct.

Seventeen elements are generally classified as nonmetals. Eleven are gases: hydrogen (H), helium (He), nitrogen (N), oxygen (O), fluorine (F), neon (Ne), chlorine (Cl), argon (Ar), krypton (Kr), xenon (Xe) and radon (Rn). One nonmetal is a liquid – bromine (Br) – and five are solids: carbon (C), phosphorus (P), sulfur (S), selenium (Se), and iodine (I).

Alkali metals (Group IA) include lithium (Li), potassium (K), sodium (Na), rubidium (Rb), cesium (Cs), and francium (Fr).

Alkali metals lose one electron to become +1 cations, and the resulting ion has a complete octet of valence electrons.

Alkaline earth metals (Group IIA) include beryllium (Be), magnesium (Mg), calcium (Ca), strontium (Sr), barium (Ba), and radium (Ra). Alkaline earth metals lose two electrons to become +2 cations, and the resulting ion has a complete octet of valence electrons.

39. C is correct.

The atom has 47 protons, 47 electrons, and 60 neutrons.

Because the periodic table is arranged by atomic number (Z), the fastest way to identify an element is to determine its atomic number. The atomic number is equal to the number of protons or electrons, which means that this atom's atomic number is 47. Use this information to locate element #47 in the table, which is Ag (silver).

Check the atomic mass (A), equal to the atomic number + number of neutrons.

For this atom, the mass is $60 + 47 = 107$.

The mass of Ag on the periodic table is listed as 107.87, which is the average mass of all Ag isotopes.

Usually, all isotopes of an element have similar masses (within 1-3 amu).

40. D is correct.

The three coordinates that come from Schrodinger's wave equations are the principal (n), angular (l), and magnetic (m) quantum numbers.

These quantum numbers describe the size, shape, and orientation of the orbitals.

The principal quantum number (n) describes the size of the orbital, the energy of an electron, and the most probable distance from the nucleus.

==

Practice Set 3: Questions 41–60

==

41. B is correct.

The atomic number (Z) is the sum of protons in an atom, which determines an element's chemical properties and location on the periodic table.

The mass number (A) is the sum of protons and neutrons in an atom.

The mass number approximates the atomic weight of the element as amu (grams per mole).

Atomic mass – atomic number = number of neutrons

$9 - 4 = 5$ neutrons

42. A is correct.

Electrons are the negatively-charged particles (charge –1) located in the electron cloud, orbiting around the atom's nucleus. Electrons are tiny particles, much smaller than protons and neutrons, and they have a mass of about 5×10^{-4} amu.

43. D is correct.

A compound consists of two or more different atoms that associate via chemical bonds.

Calcium chloride ($CaCl_2$) is an ionic compound of calcium and chloride.

Dichloromethane has the molecular formula of CH_2Cl_2

Dichlorocalcium exists as a hydrate with the molecular formula of $CaCl_2 \cdot (H_2O)_2$.

Carbon chloride (i.e., carbon tetrachloride) has the molecular formula of CCl_4.

Dicalcium chloride is not the proper IUPAC name for calcium chloride ($CaCl_2$).

---

44. A is correct.

Congeners are chemical substances related by origin, structure, or function. Regarding the periodic table, congeners are the same group elements that share similar properties (e.g., copper, silver, and gold are congeners of Group 11).

Stereoisomers, diastereomers, and epimers are terms commonly used in organic chemistry.

Stereoisomers: are chiral molecules (attached to 4 different substituents and are non-superimposable mirror images. They have the same molecular formula and the same sequence of bonded atoms but are oriented differently in 3-D space (e.g., *R* / *S* enantiomers).

Diastereomers are chiral molecules that are not mirror images. The most common form is a chiral molecule with more than 1 chiral center.

Additionally, *cis* / *trans* (*Z* / *E*) geometric isomers are also diastereomers.

Epimers: diastereomers that differ in absolute configuration at only one chiral center.

Anomers: is a type of stereoisomer used in carbohydrate chemistry to describe the orientation of the glycosidic bond of adjacent saccharides (e.g., α and β linkage of sugars). A refers to the hydroxyl group – of the anomeric carbon – pointing downward while β points upward.

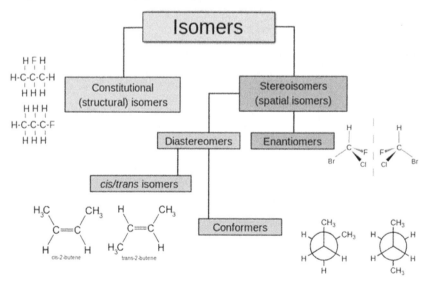

Summary of isomers

45. D is correct.

A group (or family) is a vertical column, and elements within each group share similar properties.

A period is a horizontal row in the periodic table of elements.

46. A is correct.

Metals, except mercury, are solids under normal conditions.

Potassium has the lowest melting point of the solid metals at 146 °F.

The relatively low melting temperature for potassium is due to its fourth shell ($n = 4$), which means its valence electrons are further from the nucleus; therefore, there is less attraction between its electrons and protons.

47. E is correct.

Alkaline earth metals (Group IIA) include beryllium (Be), magnesium (Mg), calcium (Ca), strontium (Sr), barium (Ba), and radium (Ra). Alkaline earth metals lose two electrons to become +2 cations, and the resulting ion has a complete octet of valence electrons.

Transition metals (or transition elements) are elements with a partially-filled d or f subshell in a common oxidative state.

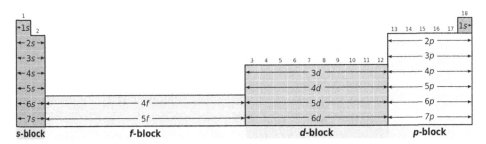

Transition metals occur in groups (vertical columns) 3–12. They occur in periods (horizontal rows) 4–7. This group includes silver, iron, and copper.

The f-block lanthanides (i.e., rare earth metals) and actinides (i.e., radioactive elements) are considered transition metals, known as inner transition metals.

Noble gases (Group VIIIA) include helium (He), neon (Ne), argon (Ar), krypton (Kr), xenon (Xe), radon (Rn), and oganesson (Og).

Alkali metals (Group IA) include lithium (Li), potassium (K), sodium (Na), rubidium (Rb), cesium (Cs), and francium (Fr). Alkali metals lose one electron to become +1 cations, and the resulting ion has a complete octet of valence electrons.

Halogens (Group VIIA) include fluorine (F), chlorine (Cl), bromine (Br), iodine (I), and astatine (At). Halogens gain one electron to become a −1 anion, and the resulting ion has a complete octet of valence electrons.

48. D is correct.

The metalloids have some properties of metals and some properties of nonmetals.

Metalloids are semimetallic elements (i.e., between metals and nonmetals). The metalloids are boron (B), silicon (Si), germanium (Ge), arsenic (As), antimony (Sb) and tellurium (Te). Some literature reports polonium (Po) and astatine (At) as metalloids.

They have properties between metals and nonmetals. They typically have a metallic appearance but are only fair conductors of electricity (as opposed to metals that are excellent conductors), making them useable in the semiconductor industry.

Metalloids tend to be brittle, and chemically they behave more like nonmetals.

However, the elements in the IIIB group are transition metals, not metalloids.

49. B is correct.

Halogens (Group VIIA) include fluorine (F), chlorine (Cl), bromine (Br), iodine (I), and astatine (At).

Halogens gain one electron to become a −1 anion, and the resulting ion has a complete octet of valence electrons.

50. A is correct.

Isotopes are variants of a particular element that differ in the number of neutrons. All isotopes of the element have the same number of protons and occupy the same position on the periodic table.

The number of protons within the atom's nucleus is the atomic number (Z) and is equal to the number of electrons in the neutral (non-ionized) atom. Each atomic number identifies a specific element, but not the isotope; an atom of a given element may have a wide range in its number of neutrons.

The number of both protons and neutrons (i.e., nucleons) in the nucleus is the atom's mass number (A), and each isotope of an element has a different mass number.

From the periodic table, the atomic mass of a natural sample of Si is 28.1, less than ^{29}Si or ^{30}Si. Therefore, ^{28}Si is the most abundant isotope.

51. E is correct.

The initial explanation was that the ray was present in the gas, and the cathode activated it.

The ray was observed even when gas was not present, so the conclusion was that the ray must have been coming from the cathode itself.

52. E is correct.

The choices correctly describe the spin quantum number (*s*).

The three coordinates that come from Schrodinger's wave equations are the principal (*n*), angular (*l*), and magnetic (*m*) quantum numbers. These quantum numbers describe the size, shape, and orientation of the orbitals in an atom.

The principal quantum number (*n*) describes the size of the orbital and the energy of an electron, and the most probable distance from the nucleus. It refers to the size of the orbital and the energy level of an electron.

The angular momentum quantum number (*l*) describes the shape of the orbitals of the subshells.

The magnetic quantum number (m) determines the number of orbitals and their orientation within a subshell. Consequently, its value depends on the orbital angular momentum quantum number (l).

Given a certain l, m is an interval ranging from $-l$ to $+l$ (i.e., it can be zero, a negative integer, or a positive integer).

The s is the spin quantum number (e.g., $+\frac{1}{2}$ or $-\frac{1}{2}$).

53. D is correct.

The three coordinates that come from Schrodinger's wave equations are the principal (n), angular (l), and magnetic (m) quantum numbers. These quantum numbers describe the size, shape, and orientation of the orbitals on an atom.

The principal quantum number (n) describes the size of the orbital and the energy of an electron, and the most probable distance from the nucleus. It refers to the size of the orbital and the energy level of an electron.

The angular momentum quantum number (l) describes the shape of the orbital of the subshells.

The magnetic quantum number (m) determines the number of orbitals and their orientation within a subshell. Consequently, its value depends on the orbital angular momentum quantum number (l).

Given a certain l, m is an interval ranging from $-l$ to $+l$ (i.e., it can be zero, a negative integer, or a positive integer).

The fourth quantum number is s, the spin quantum number (e.g., $+\frac{1}{2}$ or $-\frac{1}{2}$).

Electrons cannot be precisely located in space at any point in time, and orbitals describe probability regions for finding the electrons.

The values needed to locate an electron are n, m and l. The spin can be either $+\frac{1}{2}$ or $-\frac{1}{2}$, so four values are needed to describe a single electron.

54. A is correct.

The lowest energy orbital fills before an orbital of a higher energy level.

Aufbau principle to determine the order of energy levels in subshells:

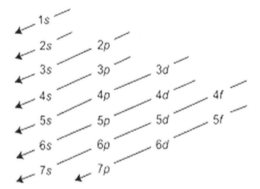

From the table above, the orbitals increase in energy from: $1s < 2s < 2p < 3s < 3p < 4s < 3d < 4p < 5s < 4d < 5p < 6s < 4f < 5d < 6p < 7s < 5f < 6d < 7p$

55. D is correct.

In general, the size of neutral atoms increases down a group (i.e., increasing shell size) and decreases from left to right across the periodic table.

Positive ions (cations) are *much smaller* than the neutral element (due to greater effective nuclear charge).

Negative ions (anions) are *much larger* (due to smaller effective nuclear charge and repulsion of valence electrons).

56. D is correct.

Boron's atomic number is 5; therefore, it contains 5 electrons.

Use the Aufbau principle to determine the order of filling orbitals.

Remember that each electron shell (principal quantum number, n) starts with a new s orbital.

57. A is correct.

Identify an element using the periodic table is its atomic number.

The atomic number is equal to the number of protons or electrons.

The total number of electrons can be determined by adding all the electrons in the provided electron configuration:

$$2 + 2 + 6 + 2 + 6 + 2 + 10 + 6 + 2 + 10 + 2 = 50.$$

Element #50 in the periodic table is tin (Sn).

58. A is correct.

Ionization energy (IE) is the amount of energy required to remove the most loosely bound electron of an isolated gaseous atom to form a cation. This is an endothermic process.

Ionization energy is expressed as:

$$X + energy \rightarrow X^+ + e^-$$

where X is an atom (or molecule) capable of being ionized (i.e., having an electron removed), X^+ is that atom or molecule after an electron is removed, and e^- is the removed electron.

The principal quantum number (n) describes the size of the orbital and the energy of an electron, and the most probable distance from the nucleus. It refers to the size of the orbital and the energy level of an electron.

The elements with larger shell sizes (n is large) listed at the bottom of the periodic table have low ionization energies. This is due to the shielding (by the inner shell electrons) from the nucleus's positive charge. The greater the distance between the electrons and the nucleus, the less energy is needed to remove the outer valence electrons.

Ionization energy decreases with increasing shell size (i.e., n value) and generally increases to the right across a period (i.e., row) in the periodic table.

Argon (Ar) has an atomic number of 18 and a shell size of $n = 3$.

Strontium (Sr) has an atomic number of 38 and a shell size of $n = 5$.

Bromine (Br) has an atomic number of 35 and a shell size of $n = 4$.

Indium (In) has an atomic number of 49 and a shell size of $n = 5$.

Tin (Sn) has an atomic number of 50 and a shell size of $n = 5$.

59. A is correct.

Electronegativity is defined as the ability of an atom to attract electrons when it bonds with another atom. The most common use of electronegativity pertains to polarity along the sigma (single) bond.

The trend for increasing electronegativity within the periodic table is up and toward the right. The most electronegative atom is fluorine (F), while the least electronegative atom is francium (Fr).

The greater the difference in electronegativity between two atoms, the more polar the bond is.

The atom with the higher electronegativity is the partial (delta) negative end of the dipole.

60. C is correct.

Seventeen elements are generally classified as nonmetals.

Eleven are gases: hydrogen (H), helium (He), nitrogen (N), oxygen (O), fluorine (F), neon (Ne), chlorine (Cl), argon (Ar), krypton (Kr), xenon (Xe) and radon (Rn).

One nonmetal is a liquid – bromine (Br).

Five are solids: carbon (C), phosphorus (P), sulfur (S), selenium (Se), and iodine (I).

Metals, except mercury, are solids under normal conditions. Potassium has the lowest melting point of the solid metals at 146 °F.

Notes

==

Practice Set 4: Questions 61–80

==

61. D is correct.

When an electron absorbs energy, it moves temporarily to a higher energy level. It drops to its initial state (also known as a ground state) while emitting the excess energy. This emission can be observed as visible spectrum lines.

Protons do not move between energy levels, so they do not absorb or emit energy.

62. B is correct.

The three coordinates that come from Schrodinger's wave equations are the principal (n), angular (l), and magnetic (m) quantum numbers. These quantum numbers describe the size, shape, and orientation of the orbitals.

The principal quantum number (n) describes the size of the orbital, the energy of an electron, and the most probable distance from the nucleus.

The angular momentum quantum number (l) describes the shape of the orbital of the subshells.

The magnetic quantum number (m) determines the number of orbitals and their orientation within a subshell. Consequently, its value depends on the orbital angular momentum quantum number (l).

Given a certain l, m is an interval ranging from $-l$ to $+l$ (i.e., it can be zero, a negative integer, or a positive integer). l must be less than n, while m_l must be less than or equal to l.

63. C is correct.

The mass number (A) is the total number of nucleons (i.e., protons and neutrons) in an atom.

The atomic number (Z) is the number of protons in an atom.

The number of neutrons in an atom can be calculated by subtracting the atomic number (Z) from the mass number (A).

Mass number – atomic number = number of neutrons

---

64. B is correct.

A compound consists of two or more different types of atoms which associate via chemical bonds.

An element is a pure chemical substance that consists of a single type of atom, defined by its atomic number (Z), the number of protons.

118 elements have been identified, of which the first 94 occur naturally on Earth.

65. E is correct.

Alkali metals (Group IA) include lithium (Li), potassium (K), sodium (Na), rubidium (Rb), cesium (Cs), and francium (Fr).

Alkaline earth metals (Group IIA) include beryllium (Be), magnesium (Mg), calcium (Ca), strontium (Sr), barium (Ba), and radium (Ra).

Halogens (Group VIIA) include fluorine (F), chlorine (Cl), bromine (Br), iodine (I), and astatine (At). Halogens gain one electron to become –1 anion, and the resulting ion has a complete octet of valence electrons.

Noble gases (group VIIIA) include helium (He), neon (Ne), argon (Ar), krypton (Kr), xenon (Xe), radon (Rn), and oganesson (Og).

Except for helium (which has a complete octet with 2 electrons, $1s^2$), the noble gases have complete octets with ns^2 and np^6 orbitals.

The representative elements are groups IA and IIA (on the left) and groups IIIA – VIIIA (on the right).

Polonium (Po) is element 84 is highly radioactive, with no stable isotopes, and is classified as either a metalloid or a metal.

66. B is correct.

Metalloids are semimetallic elements (i.e., between metals and nonmetals). The metalloids are boron (B), silicon (Si), germanium (Ge), arsenic (As), antimony (Sb), and tellurium (Te). Some literature reports polonium (Po) and astatine (At) as metalloids.

They have properties between metals and nonmetals. They typically have a metallic appearance but are only fair conductors of electricity (as opposed to metals that are excellent conductors), making them useable in the semiconductor industry.

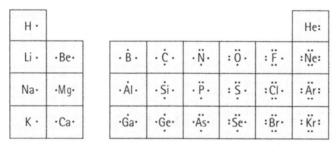

Lewis dot structures showing valence electrons for elements

Metalloids tend to be brittle, and chemically they behave more like nonmetals.

Alkali metals (Group IA) include lithium (Li), potassium (K), sodium (Na), rubidium (Rb), cesium (Cs), and francium (Fr).

Alkaline earth metals (Group IIA) include beryllium (Be), magnesium (Mg), calcium (Ca), strontium (Sr), barium (Ba), and radium (Ra).

Seventeen elements are generally classified as nonmetals. Eleven are gases: hydrogen (H), helium (He), nitrogen (N), oxygen (O), fluorine (F), neon (Ne), chlorine (Cl), argon (Ar), krypton (Kr), xenon (Xe) and radon (Rn). One nonmetal is a liquid – bromine (Br) – and five are solids: carbon (C), phosphorus (P), sulfur (S), selenium (Se), and iodine (I).

Nonmetals tend to be highly volatile (i.e., easily vaporized), have low elasticity, and are good insulators of heat and electricity.

Nonmetals tend to have high ionization energy and electronegativity and share (or gain) an electron when bonding with other elements.

Halogens (Group VIIA) include fluorine (F), chlorine (Cl), bromine (Br), iodine (I), and astatine (At).

Halogens gain one electron to become a –1 anion, and the resulting ion has a complete octet of valence electrons.

67. D is correct.

In general, the size of neutral atoms increases down a group (i.e., increasing shell size) and decreases from left to right across the periodic table.

Positive ions (cations) are *much smaller* than the neutral element (due to greater effective nuclear charge)

Negative ions (anions) are *much larger* (due to smaller effective nuclear charge and repulsion of valence electrons).

Sulfur (S, atomic number = 16) is smaller than aluminum (Al, atomic number = 13) due to the increase in the number of protons (effective nuclear charge) from left to right across a period (i.e., horizontal rows).

Al^{3+} has the same electronic configuration as Ne ($1s^2 2s^2 2p^6$) compared to Al ($1s^2 2s^2 2p^6 3s^2 3p^1$).

68. A is correct.

The valence shell is the outermost shell (i.e., highest principal quantum number, n) of an atom.

Valence electrons are those electrons of the outermost electron shell that can participate in a chemical bond.

The number of valence electrons for an element can be determined by its group (i.e., vertical column) on the periodic table.

Except for the transition metals (i.e., groups 3-12), the group number identifies how many valence electrons are associated with a particular element: all elements of the same group have the same number of valence electrons.

69. B is correct.

The semimetallic elements are arsenic (As), antimony (Sb), bismuth (Bi), and graphite (a crystalline form of carbon). Arsenic and antimony are also considered metalloids (along with boron, silicon, germanium, and tellurium), but the terms semimetal and metalloid are not synonymous.

Semimetals, in contrast to metalloids, can also be chemical compounds.

70. C is correct.

Noble gases (Group VIIIA) include helium (He), neon (Ne), argon (Ar), krypton (Kr), xenon (Xe), radon (Rn), and oganesson (Og).

Except for helium (which has a complete octet with 2 electrons, $1s^2$), the noble gases have complete octets with ns^2 and np^6 orbitals.

The metalloids are boron (B), silicon (Si), germanium (Ge), arsenic (As), antimony (Sb), and tellurium (Te). Some literature reports polonium (Po) and astatine (At) as metalloids.

71. D is correct.

Isotopes are variants of a particular element that differ in the number of neutrons. All isotopes of the element have the same number of protons and occupy the same position on the periodic table.

The experimental results should depend on the mass of the gas molecules.

Deuterium (D or ^{2}H) is known as heavy hydrogen. It is one of two stable isotopes of hydrogen. The deuterium nucleus contains one proton and one neutron, compared to H, which has 1 proton and 0 neutrons. The mass of deuterium is 2.0141 daltons, compared to 1.0078 daltons for hydrogen.

Based on the difference of mass between the isotopes, the density, gas effusion rate, and atomic vibrations would be different.

72. E is correct.

Elements are defined by the number of protons (i.e., atomic number).

The isotopes are neutral atoms: # electrons = # protons.

Isotopes are variants of a particular element that differ in the number of neutrons. All isotopes of the element have the same number of protons and occupy the same position on the periodic table.

The superscript on the left denotes the number of protons and neutrons.

Since naturally occurring lithium has a mass of 6.9 g/mol and both protons and neutrons have approximately 1 g/mol, ^{7}lithium is the predominant isotope.

73. A is correct.

The charge on 1 electron is negative.

One mole of electrons:

> Avogadro's number $\times$ e⁻.

> $(6.02 \times 10^{23}) \times (1.60 \times 10^{-19}) = 96{,}485$ coulombs (values are rounded).

74. E is correct.

Each orbital can hold two electrons.

> The *f* subshell has 7 orbitals and can accommodate 14 electrons.

> The *d* subshell has 5 lobed orbitals and can accommodate 10 electrons.

> The $n = 3$ shell contains only *s*, *p* and *d* subshells.

75. B is correct.

Ionization energy (IE) is the amount of energy required to remove the most loosely bound electron of an isolated gaseous atom to form a cation. This is an endothermic process.

Ionization energy is expressed as:

> $X + \text{energy} \rightarrow X^+ + e^-$

where X is an atom (or molecule) capable of being ionized (i.e., having an electron removed), X^+ is that atom or molecule after an electron is removed, and e^- is the removed electron.

The principal quantum number (*n*) describes the size of the orbital and the energy of an electron, and the most probable distance from the nucleus. It refers to the size of the orbital and the energy level of an electron.

The elements with larger shell sizes (*n* is large) listed at the bottom of the periodic table have low ionization energies. This is due to the shielding (by the inner shell electrons) from the nucleus's positive charge.

The greater the distance between the electrons and the nucleus, the less energy is needed to remove the outer valence electrons.

Ionization energy decreases with increasing shell size (i.e., *n* value) and generally increases to the right across a period (i.e., row) in the periodic table.

Chlorine (Cl) has an atomic number of 10 and a shell size of $n = 3$.

Francium (Fr) has an atomic number of 87 and a shell size of $n = 7$.

Gallium (Ga) has an atomic number of 31 and a shell size of $n = 4$.

Iodine (I) has an atomic number of 53 and a shell size of $n = 5$.

Cesium (Cs) has an atomic number of 55 and a shell size of $n = 6$.

76. D is correct.

Electrons are electrostatically (i.e., negative and positive charge) attracted to the nucleus. An atom's electrons generally occupy outer shells only if other electrons have already filled the more inner shells. However, there are exceptions to this rule, with some atoms having two or even three incomplete outer shells.

1s
2s 2p
3s 3p 3d
4s 4p 4d 4f
5s 5p 5d 5f ...
6s 6p 6d ... ...

The Aufbau (German for building up) principle is based on the Madelung rule to fill the subshells based on the lowest energy.

77. C is correct.

In Bohr's model of the atom, electrons can jump to higher energy levels, gain energy, or drop to lower energy levels, releasing energy.

When an electric current flows through an element in the gas phase, glowing light is produced.

By directing this light through a prism, a pattern of lines known as the atomic spectra can be seen.

These lines are produced by excited electrons dropping to lower energy levels. Since each element's energy levels are different, each element has a unique set of lines it produces, which is why the spectrum is called the "atomic fingerprint" of the element.

78. E is correct.

Obtain the atomic number of Mn from the periodic table.

Mn is a transition metal, located in Group VIIB/7; atomic number is 25.

Use the Aufbau principle to fill up the orbitals of Mn: $1s^2 2s^2 2p^6 3s^2 3p^6 4s^2 3d^5$

The transition metals occur in groups 3–12 (vertical columns) of the periodic table. They occur in periods 4–7 (horizontal rows).

Transition metals are defined as elements that have a partially-filled d or f subshell in a common oxidative state. This group of elements includes silver, iron, and copper.

The transition metals are elements whose atom has an incomplete d sub-shell or can give rise to cations with an incomplete d sub-shell. By this definition, all of the elements in groups 3–11 (or 12 by some literature) are transition metals.

The transition elements have characteristics that are not found in other elements, resulting from the partially filled d shell. These include the formation of compounds whose color is due to d–d electronic transitions, the formation of compounds in many oxidation states due to the relatively low reactivity of unpaired d electrons.

The transition elements form many paramagnetic (i.e., attracted to an externally applied magnetic field) compounds due to the presence of unpaired d electrons. By exception to their unique traits, a few compounds of main group elements are also paramagnetic (e.g., nitric oxide and oxygen).

79. E is correct.

Electronegativity is defined as the ability of an atom to attract electrons when it bonds with another atom. The most common use of electronegativity pertains to polarity along the sigma (single) bond.

The trend for increasing electronegativity within the periodic table is up and toward the right. The most electronegative atom is fluorine (F), while the least electronegative atom is francium (Fr).

80. C is correct.

Alkali metals (Group IA) include lithium (Li), potassium (K), sodium (Na), rubidium (Rb), cesium (Cs), and francium (Fr).

Alkali metals lose one electron to become +1 cations, and the resulting ion has a complete octet of valence electrons.

Alkaline earth metals (Group IIA) include beryllium (Be), magnesium (Mg), calcium (Ca), strontium (Sr), barium (Ba), and radium (Ra).

Alkaline earth metals lose two electrons to become +2 cations, and the resulting ion has a complete octet of valence electrons.

Notes

===

Practice Set 5: Questions 81–104

===

81. C is correct.

The mass number (A) is the sum of protons and neutrons in an atom.

The mass number approximates the atomic weight of the element as amu (grams per mole).

The problem already provides the mass number: ^{79}Br has a mass number of 79.

The atomic number of ^{79}Br can be obtained from the periodic table. Br is in group VIIA/17, and its atomic number is 35.

82. A is correct.

The mass number (A) is the total number of nucleons (i.e., protons and neutrons) in an atom.

The superscript on the left denotes the number of protons and neutrons.

The atomic number (Z) is the number of protons in an atom.

The number of neutrons in an atom can be calculated by subtracting the atomic number (Z) from the mass number (A).

83. C is correct.

An element is a pure chemical substance that consists of a single type of atom, distinguished by its atomic number (Z) (i.e., the number of protons it contains). One hundred eighteen elements have been identified, of which the first 94 occur naturally on Earth, with the remaining 24 being synthetic elements.

The properties of the elements on the periodic table repeat at regular intervals, creating "groups" or "families" of elements. Each column on the periodic table is a group, and elements within each group have similar physical and chemical characteristics due to the orbital location of their outermost electron. These groups only exist because the elements of the periodic table are listed by increasing atomic number.

84. B is correct.

Alkali metals (Group IA) include lithium (Li), potassium (K), sodium (Na), rubidium (Rb), cesium (Cs), and francium (Fr).

Alkali metals lose one electron to become +1 cations, and the resulting ion has a complete octet of valence electrons.

The alkali metals have low electronegativity and react violently with water (e.g., the violent reaction of metallic sodium with water).

85. A is correct.

Seventeen elements are generally classified as nonmetals. Eleven are gases: hydrogen (H), helium (He), nitrogen (N), oxygen (O), fluorine (F), neon (Ne), chlorine (Cl), argon (Ar), krypton (Kr), xenon (Xe) and radon (Rn).

One nonmetal is a liquid – bromine (Br).

Five nonmetals are solids: carbon (C), phosphorus (P), sulfur (S), selenium (Se), and iodine (I).

Nonmetals tend to be highly volatile (i.e., easily vaporized), have low elasticity, and are good insulators of heat and electricity.

Nonmetals tend to have high ionization energy and electronegativity and share (or gain) an electron when bonding with other elements.

86. E is correct.

Group VIA (16) has three nonmetals: oxygen, sulfur, and selenium.

Metalloids are semimetallic elements (i.e., between metals and nonmetals). The metalloids are boron (B), silicon (Si), germanium (Ge), arsenic (As), antimony (Sb), and tellurium (Te).

Some literature reports polonium (Po) and astatine (At) as metalloids.

87. C is correct.

Transition metals (or transition elements) are defined as elements with a partially-filled *d* or *f* subshell in a common oxidative state.

Transition metals occur in groups (vertical columns) 3–12 of the period table. They occur in periods (horizontal rows) 4–7. This group of elements includes silver, iron, and copper.

The *f*-block lanthanides (i.e., rare earth metals) and actinides (i.e., radioactive elements) are also considered *transition metals* and are known *as inner transition metals*.

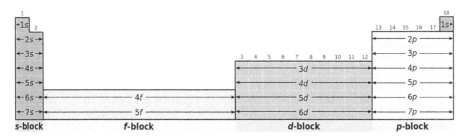

Transition elements have characteristics that are not found in other elements, resulting from the partially filled *d* shell. These include the formation of compounds whose color is due to *d* electronic transitions, the formation of compounds in many oxidation states due to the relatively low reactivity of unpaired *d* electrons. The incomplete *d* sub-shell can give rise to cations with an incomplete *d* sub-shell.

Transition elements form many paramagnetic (i.e., attracted to an externally applied magnetic field) compounds due to the presence of unpaired *d* and *f* electrons. A few compounds of main group elements are also paramagnetic (e.g., nitric oxide and oxygen).

88. E is correct.

An element is a pure chemical substance that consists of a single type of atom, distinguished by its atomic number (Z) for the number of protons.

118 elements have been identified, of which the first 94 occur naturally on Earth.

89. B is correct.

Isotopes are variants of an element that differ in the number of neutrons.

All isotopes of the element have the same number of protons and occupy the same position on the periodic table.

Alpha decay results in the loss of two protons.

Beta-decay is a type of radioactive decay in which a neutron is transformed into a proton, or a proton is transformed into a neutron.

Since isotopes of the same element have the same number of protons (Z), the number of protons lost by α decay must equal the number gained by β decay.

Therefore, twice as many β decays as α decays occurs for a ratio of 1:2 for α to β decay.

90. B is correct.

Elements are defined by the number of protons (i.e., atomic number).

The isotopes are neutral atoms: # electrons = # protons.

Isotopes are variants of a particular element that differ in the number of neutrons. All isotopes of the element have the same number of protons and occupy the same position on the periodic table.

Cu has an atomic weight of 63.5 grams.

Therefore, the other isotope of Cu must be heavier than the more common ^{63}Cu, and the atomic weight is closer to 65.

91. E is correct.

A cathode-ray particle is another name for an electron.

Those particles (i.e., electrons) are attracted to the positively charged cathode, which implies that they are negatively charged.

92. A is correct.

Pauli exclusion principle is the quantum principle that states that two identical electrons cannot have the same four quantum numbers: the principal quantum number (n), the angular momentum quantum number (l), the magnetic quantum number (m_ℓ), and the spin quantum number (m_s).

For two electrons in the same orbital (n, m_ℓ, and l), the spin quantum number (m_s) must be different, and the electrons must have opposite half-integer spins (i.e., $+\frac{1}{2}$ and $-\frac{1}{2}$).

Hund's rule describes that the electrons enter each orbital of a given type singly and with identical spins before any pairing of electrons of the opposite spin occurs within those orbitals.

Heisenberg's uncertainty principle states that it is impossible to accurately determine both the momentum and the position of an electron simultaneously.

93. E is correct.

The atom's second electron is $n = 2$; it has 2 orbitals: s, p

Each orbital can hold two electrons.

Maximum number of electrons in $n = 2$ shell is:

The s subshell has 1 spherical orbital and accommodates 2 electrons.

The p subshell has 3 dumbbell-shaped orbitals and accommodates 6 e.

Total number of electrons:

2 (for s) + 6 (for p) = 8 electrons

94. D is correct.

Each orbital can hold two electrons.

5 d orbitals can accommodate a total of 10 electrons.

95. D is correct.

The number of orbitals in a subshell is different from the maximum number of electrons in the subshell. The f subshell has 7 orbitals (14 electrons).

96. A is correct.

Only photons are released as electrons move from higher to lower energy orbitals.

Alpha particles are helium nuclei, and beta particles are electrons.

Gamma rays (i.e., gamma radiation) are ionizing radiation produced from the decay of an atomic nucleus from a high energy state to a lower energy state. They are biologically hazardous.

97. B is correct.

According to the Bohr model and quantum theory, the electron's energy levels occur at quantified and calculable energies. For hydrogen, the energy of each level is found by:

$$E = -13.6 \text{ eV/n}^2$$

The negative sign by convention indicates that this is the energy needed to ionize the electron completely.

When promoted by absorbing energy, an electron can be at higher energy levels.

98. E is correct.

Ions often have the same electronic configuration (i.e., isoelectronic) as neutral atoms of a different element (e.g., F^- is isoelectronic with Ne). However, this is not always valid for elements with electrons in excited states.

An ion can have an electron configuration that is consistent with the rules of quantum numbers.

99. A is correct.

Consider the last 2 orbitals: $3s^23p^6$.

This means that the atom's valence electrons are $2 + 6 = 8$ electrons.

Atoms with 8 valence electrons (i.e., complete octet) are very stable – chemically inert.

100. C is correct.

Ionization energy (IE) is the amount of energy required to remove the most loosely bound electron of an isolated gaseous atom to form a cation. This is an endothermic process.

Ionization energy is expressed as: $X + energy \rightarrow X^+ + e^-$

where X is an atom (or molecule) capable of being ionized (i.e., having an electron removed), X^+ is that atom or molecule after an electron is removed, and e^- is the removed electron.

The principal quantum number (n) describes the size of the orbital and the energy of an electron, and the most probable distance from the nucleus. It refers to the size of the orbital and the energy level of an electron.

The elements with larger shell sizes (n is large) listed at the bottom of the periodic table have low ionization energies. This is due to the shielding (by the inner shell electrons) from the nucleus's positive charge. The greater the distance between the electrons and the nucleus, the less energy is needed to remove the outer valence electrons.

Halogens have high ionization energy because they have 7 electrons; they only need to gain one more electron to reach stability (i.e., complete octet). Therefore, halogens have a large electron affinity, which measures the tendency for ions to gain electrons. More energy is required to remove the 7th electron (compared to the 1st or 2nd electrons, such as for elements in group IA or IIA).

101. D is correct.

Chlorine completes its octet when it gains an electron, so chlorine atoms form anions (i.e., gain electrons) much more easily than cations (i.e., lose electrons).

102. B is correct.

The mass number (A) is the sum of protons and neutrons in an atom.

The mass number approximates the atomic weight of the element as amu (grams per mole).

103. A is correct.

H's atomic mass is 1.0 amu, and a single proton has a mass of 1 amu, the most common isotope contains no neutrons.

From acid-base chemistry, hydrogen ions are referred to as *protons* (H$^+$) with zero neutrons in the nucleus.

104. A is correct.

Oxygen contains only *s* and *p* orbitals and cannot form six bonds due to the lack of *d* orbitals.

Second-period elements lack *d* orbitals and cannot have more than four bonds to the central atom.

Customer Satisfaction Guarantee

Your feedback is important because we provide the highest quality educational materials. Email us your comments.

info@sterling–prep.com

*We reply to all emails – **check your spam folder***

Notes

Notes

Notes

Notes

Essential Chemistry Self-Teaching Guide series

- Electronic Structure and the Periodic Table

- Chemical Bonding

- Phases and Phase Equilibria

- Stoichiometry

- Kinetics and Equilibrium in Chemical Reactions

- Acids and Bases

- Solution Chemistry

- Thermochemistry and Thermodynamics

- Electrochemistry

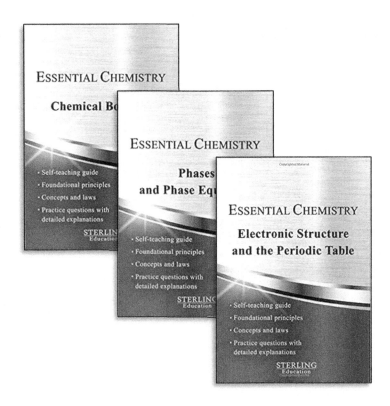

Essential Physics Self-Teaching Guide series

- Kinematics and Dynamics

- Equilibrium and Momentum

- Force, Motion, Gravitation

- Work and Energy

- Fluids and Solids

- Waves and Periodic Motion

- Light and Optics

- Sound

- Electrostatics and Electromagnetism

- Electric Circuits

- Heat and Thermodynamics

- Atomic and Nuclear Structure

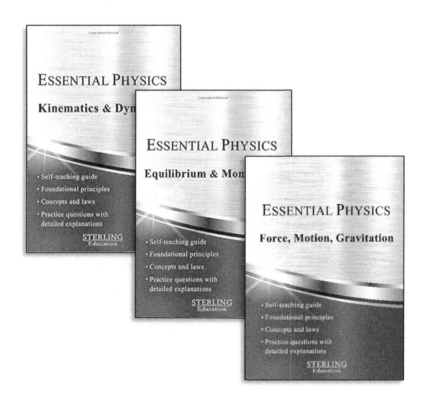

Essential Biology Self-Teaching Guide series

- Eukaryotic Cell: Structure and Function
- Enzymes and Cellular Metabolism
- DNA, Protein Synthesis, Gene Expression
- Specialized Eukaryotic Cells
- Genetics
- Nervous System
- Endocrine System
- Circulatory System
- Respiratory System
- Lymphatic and Immune System
- Digestive System
- Excretory System
- Skeletal System
- Muscle System
- Integumentary System
- Reproductive System
- Development
- Microbiology
- Plants
- Photosynthesis
- Evolution, Classification, Diversity
- Ecosystems and Biosphere
- Population and Community Ecology

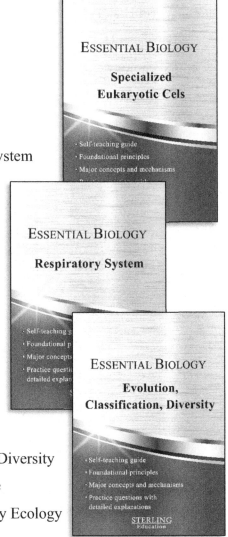

Everything You Always Wanted to Know About...

- American History

- American Law

- American Government and Politics

- Comparative Government and Politics

- World History

- European History

- Psychology

- Environmental Science

- Human Geography

Made in the USA
Columbia, SC
24 April 2021